A DOCTOR'S WITNESS:
FROM A CULTURE OF LIFE TO A CULTURE OF DEATH

By, Robert A. Dolehide, M.D.
with Cynthia R. Nicolosi

D1366452

Graphics:
Pete Massari
Rockford, IL 61114

Editorial Assistance:
Cynthia Nicolosi

Published by CMJ Marian Publishers and Distributors:
Post Office Box 661
Oak Lawn, Illinois 60454
http://www.cmjbooks.com
jwby@aol.com
Phone: 708-636-2995
Fax: 708-636-2855

Why the symbol of medicine on the front cover? In North America, the Caduceus has long been associated with health care and medicine. Its history is based primarily on Greek Mythology and the Greek physician, Hippocrates. For 2500 years, the Hippocratic Oath has guided, guarded, and grounded the medical profession. It has called physicians to be defenders of life.

At Pope Francis's meeting with the International Federation of Catholic Medicine Association, he firmly reiterated, "The ultimate aim of medicine remains the defense and protection of life." The Hippocratic Oath, as used in the past, is now broken. The Holy Father asks all medical professionals to "bear witness to the culture of life."

Printed in the United States of America

Fr. John A. Hardon, S.J.

Dedication

I dedicate this book to the memory of Fr. John Hardon, Servant of God. He was a true witness to Christian love by his service to the souls God put in his life.

A Fascinating read....

"A Doctor's Witness" is a fascinating read for any of Dr. Dolehide's peers as well as those interested in the impact that Catholicism has or should have on the fabric of public service. Dolehide was there amidst the glory days and throughout societal change that has marked the health care industry for untold years to come. Some of the change is welcome; other changes are troublesome relative to the capacity of doctors and adjoining professionals to be truly witnesses to the treasured virtues and heroism of the health profession.

Most Reverend Joseph N. Perry
Auxiliary Bishop
Archdiocese of Chicago

The Hippocratic Oath

I swear by Apollo the physician, and Asclepius, and Hygeia and Panacea and all the gods and goddesses as my witnesses, that, according to my ability and judgment, I will keep this Oath and this contract:

To hold him who taught me this art equally dear to me as my parents, to be a partner in life with him, and to fulfill his needs when required; to look upon his offspring as equals to my own siblings, and to teach them this art, if they shall wish to learn it, without fee or contract; and that by the set rules, lectures, and every other mode of instruction, I will impart a knowledge of the art to my own sons, and those of my teachers, and to students bound by this contract and having sworn this Oath to the law of medicine, but to no others.

I will use those dietary regimens which will benefit my patients according to my greatest ability and judgment, and I will do no harm or injustice to them.

I will not give a lethal drug to anyone if I am asked, nor will I advise such a plan; and similarly I will not give a woman a pessary to cause an abortion.

In purity and according to divine law will I carry out my life and my art.

I will not use the knife, even upon those suffering from stones, but I will leave this to those who are trained in this craft.

Into whatever homes I go, I will enter them for the benefit of the sick, avoiding any voluntary act of impropriety or corruption, including the seduction of women or men, whether they are free men or slaves.

Whatever I see or hear in the lives of my patients, whether in connection with my professional practice or not, which ought not to be spoken of outside, I will keep secret, as considering all such things to be private.

So long as I maintain this Oath faithfully and without corruption, may it be granted to me to partake of life fully and the practice of my art, gaining the respect of all men for all time.

However, should I transgress this Oath and violate it, may the opposite be my fate.[1]

---

[1] Translated by Michael North, National Library of Medicine, 2002. Available at http://www.nlm.nih.gov/hmd/greek/greek_oath.html.

Table of Contents

PREFACE

More than fifty years ago, Fr. John Hardon, S. J., Servant of God, asked me to write a book on the practice of medicine and the Catholic faith. The time has come to follow through on his request.

In truth, the book Fr. Hardon wanted could only be written now because it required a lifetime of medical practice to arrive at the wisdom necessary to tackle the age-old question of whether science and faith can co-exist in a single individual's moral fabric. A book of this kind must illustrate the integration of spiritual values with material and temporal values. Philosophers have struggled for eons to express this synthesis – how much more would I, a practical man of science!

Philosophy, however, is not the principle approach I will take in the following pages. Instead, I will describe what I know: life on the ground. As a Catholic layman, I will share what I have witnessed in a half century of medical practice. What I will offer the reader is a description of actual events in the life of one physician who has witnessed nothing short of a revolution in the medical profession. I will recall the stories that are significant to me, and I will reflect on those narratives in light of my Christian faith.

This book, then, answers Fr. Hardon's appeal not only in its presentation of a medical practice conceived in and guided by the principles of faith, but also insofar as the author has been witness to the divorce of such principles from medicine. Over the course of my career, I have watched as the traditional values of the medical profession, expressed in the Hippocratic Oath, gradually gave way to a new ethos that placed profit over service and pride over obedience to a divinely instituted natural order. Advances in medical technology made it possible for physicians to literally "play God," meeting the needs and desires of their patients to a degree never before possible.

My concern here is not to capture a by-gone, golden age. I hope with these recollections to encourage reflection on how the medical profession can escape from the mire of lies into which it has fallen. The backward glance here may help answer some fundamental questions. How can a Christian physician today meld the current approach to medical care with values that reach back two millennia? How can he or she share the sensibilities of the apostolic physician Saint Luke and the countless holy souls who, in the name of Christ, embraced the vocation of caring for the sick and dying? How does a medical practitioner stay spiritually healthy in the midst of a profession that wields such awesome powers to heal, yet so often remains blind to the true goods of human life?

I have spent the better part of my life and career in pursuit of answers to these questions. I was born into a Catholic family and raised in a world permeated by Christian ideals. The gift of faith I received in baptism grew in a cultural context that supported and nourished it. The world, however, changed rapidly beneath my feet as I left childhood behind. Depression, war, and the ideologies of a secular order wore away at traditional values and ways of living. In the midst of this cultural upheaval, I formulated and embraced a single principle that would guide me all my days. It guided me through military service in World War II, the challenges of medical studies and internship, and finally served as the cornerstone of my practice. In sum, I looked upon the human being as much more than a body. I believed and acted upon the belief that the human being is composed of body and soul.

Principles are important. We act on the basis of our principles even when we might have difficulty stating them. Medical practitioners put their principles into action every time they approach a patient. These principles determine what kind of care they will give. The words of the Hippocratic Oath tell us that from ancient times, medicine has been concerned with the protection of life and governed by the principle "do no harm." Christianity took the natural pagan values of the Oath and elevated them in light of the Incarnation and the promised gifts of the Holy Spirit. For a Christian doctor, the Hippocratic Oath was not replaced, but fulfilled by the Gospel. In the Christian schema, every human life comes from a special creative act of God. No matter how long or how brief its time on earth, the human spirit eventually returns to its eternal source. Human life is precious in the eyes of Christian physicians precisely because of its sacred origin and end. Consequently, for a Christian, the medical profession is not merely an occupation, but rather, a vocation.

How far we have strayed from this vision! The Hippocratic Oath has become a quaint souvenir of a distant past. In place of doing no harm, doctors may now make death their aim. Medical students learn that "death-on-demand" is a good, not an evil. We are accustomed to the political debate concerning the legalization of abortion, euthanasia, and assisted suicide, but what we often forget is that each of these procedures includes the intervention of medical professionals. From the point of view of these professionals, dealing with death has become just another form of "treatment." Instead of a training that prepares them for the mission of healing, medical personnel now learn how to efficiently end a life that is inconvenient or beyond hope of recovery. Clearly, the sense of identity of a medical professional today is not the same as that embraced by ancient practitioners, pagan and Christian, who pledged themselves in the Hippocratic Oath.

On September 20, 2013, Pope Francis met with members of the International Federation of Catholic Medical Associations and spoke of the current paradox in the medical profession. "On the one hand, we see progress in the field of medicine, thanks to the work of scientists who passionately and unreservedly dedicate themselves to the search for new cures," he said. "On the other hand, however, we also encounter the risk that doctors lose sight of their identity in the service of life." The Pope went on to explain that this paradoxical situation is evident also in the fact that "while new rights are attributed to or, indeed, almost presumed by the individual, life is not always protected as the primary value and the primordial right of every human being. The ultimate aim of medicine remains the defense and promotion of life."[2]

---

[2] Available at:
http://w2.vatican.va/content/francesco/en/speeches/2013/september/documents/papa-francesco_20130920_associazioni-medici-cattolici.html.

The Holy Father's words ring true for me. In the course of a fifty-year career in medicine, I witnessed the shift from a culture of life to a culture of death. I watched as my nation's politicians and judges condemned the unborn to abortion on demand. I noted the gradual encroachment of death services such as assisted suicide and euthanasia. I worked shoulder to shoulder with medical professionals whose work became defined more by profit than the service of human good. But it was not only in the workplace that I saw the advance of a dehumanizing culture. I watched its grip extend to all aspects of family and social life. I grieved to see the rise in divorce, domestic violence, addiction, and a loss of appreciation for the common good. The values that supported a culture of faith and family steadily gave way to others advocating the self-realization of the individual at any cost.

As a parent, I had a front row seat for the implementation of socialist values in education. I fought hard to hold back the tide of secular materialism in the Catholic schools my children attended. Often, my wife and I found ourselves opposing ideas and education programs that originated with the Catholic hierarchy. Whether at work or at home, I managed to stand firm on traditional values – though it sometimes felt like I was fighting on all fronts.

In any case, it is time for this story to be told. There are signs that our culture is ready to re-examine the radical individualism and materialistic values that shaped the second half of the 20th century. Recent events have provoked a re-consideration of "pro-death" policies in government and medical care. Statistics show that the number of abortions has declined. Though some insist that easier access to contraception explains this drop, it is more likely that the common practice now of ultrasound has made it undeniably evident that a human being lives in the womb of an expectant mother. A woman who sees her unborn child flexing its fingers is unlikely to want to terminate its life. Moreover, the recent sting of Planned Parenthood's clinics has focused awareness on the brutal nature of abortion procedures. No one can pretend anymore that a fetus is merely a clump of cells. Nor can anyone maintain that abortion is only about the good of the mother. The abortion industry is clearly a money-making enterprise that profits from the death of infants. In brief, the facts are in on a culture of death, and the pendulum is poised to swing back toward life.

I hope that this memoire will provide some light for a world that has lost its way. Perhaps by retracing the path from a culture of life to a culture of death, we may be able to reverse our steps. I also wish to encourage a new generation of Christian physicians to boldly assert their faith-inspired values in the practice of medicine. May the spirit of St. Luke, that dear and glorious physician, dwell in our hearts and guide us back to Life!

Chapter One

A Faith-Informed World

*Clay has to be molded, and that is done
primarily in the family, which is more
sacred than the state. – Bishop Sheen*

Every story begins in the midst of a story already in
progress. A new human life comes into being within the
narrative of a woman's life and a couple's relationship. From
the moment of conception, each one of us begins a unique
journey that unites and carries forward the stories of two
families. Over the course of a lifetime, in fact, we are part of
many stories already in progress: local, national – even global.
The truth is that every one of us inherits and contributes to the
narratives we enter, sometimes altering them in radical ways.

The history into which I entered and made my
contribution was, for the most part, that of the Chicago area of
the State of Illinois. At the same time, the family that received
me into this world passed on to me another, more profound
history – that of Roman Catholicism. These two elements, one
geographical and the other spiritual, together provided the
narrative framework for my life. Of the two, however, Roman
Catholicism has priority. The knowledge of my true origin and
end has been the determining factor in the choices that have,
so to speak, "written" my life story.

1

The first chapter of my story began on November 19, 1925. I was the third of four children born to John and Marie Dolehide. John was the eldest, followed by Eugene four years later. My only sister, Noreen, was born three years after me.

My father's parents were both born in Ireland. They came to the states to give their children a better life. Eventually they settled in Illinois. Both my parents grew up in Chicago. My mother was born Marie Benner on the West Side of Chicago, and my father was born in the "Irish ghetto" on 55th and Ashland Avenue. They met through my mother's sister, Marguerite, at a neighborhood dance. Mom was taller than my dad and a very proper, stately woman. She was a high school graduate and a telephone operator at Cook County Hospital. My father had only an eighth grade education. He worked for thirty years as a door-to-door insurance salesman with Metropolitan Life Insurance. I remember him many nights counting change collected from clients. My father would take us on weekends to visit his family or my mother's family. On the way, we would have to stop to make a Metropolitan insurance collection – even on Sundays. My mother was always the one to manage their four fidgety offspring. Somehow, she also managed to stay involved in all the woman's clubs in the parish.

In 1935, my father moved our family of six from Decatur, Illinois, to Chicago. In Decatur, he had worked as general manager for the Metropolitan Life Insurance Company. Although he lacked the leadership training of some of the other executives in the company, he was well-regarded as an excellent leader. Hence, it came as somewhat of a shock when he was abruptly removed from his position and given a relatively obscure job at the company's Chicago office. At that time, Decatur had the reputation of being a city hostile to Catholics, so our family always suspected that the demotion and transfer may have been motivated by my father's religious beliefs. As a result of this traumatic episode, however, our family became more socially aware and deeply convinced of the value of education as a defense against intolerance. We also turned with greater faith and reliance toward Divine Providence. Times were hard after our move from Decatur. The lessons of this period in my upbringing have remained with me to this day.

It has been said that when God closes a door, he opens a window. In fact, the Chatham area of Chicago where my family landed turned out to be a far friendlier environment than the one we had known in Decatur. This was due in large part to the ethnicity of the area. We became part of a longstanding narrative of cultural diversity and traditional, Catholic values. At this time, Catholic immigrants of the first and second generations cherished their faith and passed it on to their children. Nor was this faith merely a set of ideas and doctrines. The Catholic faith was lived, visibly and tangibly, in regular celebrations of feast days and the existence of active parish organizations celebrating the saints, the professions, and the interests of men, women and young adults. What we had, in sum, was a truly Catholic culture that gave shape to our long-term and short-term goals in life.

My family's first home in the area was a two-story flat just four blocks from St. Dorothy's Catholic Church at 78th and Eberhardt in Chicago. The streets were lined with "bungalows" which all looked alike. The neighborhood was comprised of Hungarian and Irish families who lived their Catholic faith. My siblings and I attended the grammar school attached to St. Dorothy's. We were taught by the beautiful Blessed Virgin Mary nuns who remain to this day wonderful educators. From the middle of the 1930's to 1940, the enrollment at our school was the largest in its history. It's amazing to recall that in grades 5-8, the boys and girls were in separate classrooms!

Our family was matriarchal in nature. My father worked from day to night selling insurance. He was often out of town; hence, my mother carried the bulk of the daily household responsibilities. She even stoked the basement furnace. (My father did it on occasion, sometimes falling asleep in the process.) My mother was not a showy or forceful person. By simple gestures, she exercised quiet persuasion. She was loving and attentive – totally dedicated to her vocation as wife and mother.

Our family was Catholic without being pretentious. Neither of my parents made much of their piety. My mother rose each morning and, without kneeling down, said a short prayer. She ended her day in the same way. My father, too, was modest in his expressions of faith. He would tip his hat when passing a church. I remember him laying his rosary on the table before retiring. On Sundays, our family attended the 9 o'clock Children's Mass at St. Dorothy's. Tardiness for Mass resulted in the loss of our privileges the following week at school, so we children were vigilant about getting to church on time. The parish set Saturday afternoons aside for the confessions of children and youths. Adults would go later in the evening. This weekly practice of our faith, along with our observance of holy days in the liturgical year, gave a rhythm to our lives and impressed on us the ultimate purpose of this life: heaven. I remember to this day the death of Pope Pius XI, commemorated in our parish by the draping of the church in black and purple.

In 1938, due to the depression, our family lost the flat in St. Dorothy's parish and moved to a smaller apartment in the neighboring parish of St. Sabina. I was in eighth grade at the time. We made many friends at St. Sabina School and in the parish, and our mother involved herself in everything we did.

I began this chapter by asserting that our stories unfold as part of other stories. The truth is that they also unfold alongside other stories. Siblings are the first people in our lives to share our narrative journey.

My eldest brother John accompanied my mother to daily Mass during his school years. At the age of thirteen, he sought permission from my father to enter the Carmelite novitiate in Niagara, New York. My father, however, felt that he was too young. Always an exceptional student, John won four years of free tuition to any Catholic high school of his choice. He decided on De LaSalle Institute, home to four former Chicago mayors and numerous religious and civic leaders. After graduating from high school, John still hoped to enter the seminary, but my father continued to discourage the idea. Only after John had finished his studies at DePaul

University did my father relent. John became a postulant with the Dominican fathers in River Forest, Illinois. Though my father could not provide financially for John's education, the Dominican Order accepted him without question. He received the habit in 1940 at St. Thomas Aquinas Priory in River Forest.

John was ordained in 1947. He had a long and illustrious career as a priest. He ministered at the Preacher's Institute at St. Pius in Chicago and taught for a year at Fenwick High School. He also ministered in Louisiana, New Mexico, Colorado, Minnesota, Texas, and Tennessee. In 1984 he became director of the Dominican Laity, and in 1985 he became associate pastor of St. Patrick Church in McHenry, Illinois. He was transferred to St. Peter's in Geneva, Illinois, in 1988 and then to St. Catherine of Alexandria in Oak Lawn in 1991, serving his longest stint as associate pastor there until 2006. Eventually, he moved to the assisted living center at St. Pius V Priory and then to Resurrection Life Center in 2010. He was 93 years old when he died in 2011.

Like John, my brother Eugene was a very good student. He was offered scholarships to great schools. During medical school at Loyola, he hardly ever bought a textbook (too expensive), studying from his own notes instead. Eugene's pivotal moment came in 1943. Although the family had known difficult times before, my mother's decline in health that year (she had tuberculosis) precipitated our first real crisis. Dr. Karl Meyer, a nationally renowned surgeon and the Chief of Staff at Cook County Hospital, had known my mother since her days as a telephone operator at the hospital.

He performed successful surgery on her. His professional and humanitarian skills greatly impressed my brother Eugene who was in medical school at the time. It was only natural, then, that after graduation, Eugene elected to study at Cook County Hospital. He married Marceline Clark whom he met while at Cook County.

My sister Noreen was an extraordinary person in every way. She was tall, beautiful, and always impeccably dressed. Her sense of style included wearing hats – something women, sadly, don't do anymore. As a teenager, Noreen was very involved in high school and church activities. She continued living life to the full at St. Xavier University as she prepared for a career in education. Despite many challenges, Noreen always had a smile on her face. Her life revolved around faith and family. Her husband, Tom, was a patient confidant and wonderful father. As a public school teacher, she was for the most part the sole bread winner. Later in life, Noreen was very attentive to Fr. John, often watching the White Sox Games with him at her Country Club Hills home. She passed away on July 31, 2013, and is sorely missed by all of us.

Looking back at my growing up years, I have to say that we enjoyed a simpler and more pleasant life than today. Granted, every generation thinks of its times as the best of times. In this case, however, I truly believe that the years I am describing were "the good old days." For the most part, people knew who they were. Families sat together for dinner. Children said prayers and recited the pledge of allegiance in school. Mothers stayed home to look after the children. There was a solid work ethic and a sense of the common good. There was pride in our nation and confidence in our leaders, including religious leaders. Ours was a culture of high principles, hard work, and deep religious faith.

When I reflect on my schooling, one thing that stands out for me is the content of the curriculum at the parish schools we attended. Catholic teachers emphasized Church history and the catechism; they integrated the education of our minds with the practice of pious devotions and the occasional spiritual retreat. To put it simply, we were "formed" and "informed." We received a solid foundation in faith and apologetics that enabled us to keep our balance through the turbulent years of World War II and after. We were well prepared as Catholics to pass through the changes in the Church that followed Vatican Council II. Perhaps this issue stands out in my mind so much because of my experiences educating my own children. Sad to say, my wife and I spent a great deal of time debating the content of the curriculum at the Catholic schools our children attended. We witnessed – and resisted – the abandonment of traditional Catholic education. It is no wonder to me that the Church has been declining in numbers since its members are no longer prepared to meet the challenges of their faith presented by contemporary culture.

As a child, I couldn't have said what was important about the education I was receiving. I took it in as children do. It's funny the things you remember. Tuition at St. Dorothy's was $1.00 a month. Candy could be purchased across the street at Donohue's for a penny or two. And then there was Sister Sigimund. She carried a long ruler that was said to be made from six or eight different types of wood. According to older brothers and sisters, it felt twice as hard as any other ruler when it landed on you. I do not remember Sister Sigimund ever using it, but I did see it once lying on her desk. Its reputation alone made it a powerful force for classroom decorum. In any case, thanks to Sister Sigimund, I learned about something that would fascinate me for a lifetime: the apparitions of the Blessed Mother to three little children in Fatima, Portugal. As a class project, Sister had us make a small replica of the apparitions, including the three children: Lucia, Jacinta, and Francesco. Perhaps because the visionaries were children, like me, I felt a strong attraction to the story. Forty-six years later, my childhood wonder still intact, I was to see the actual site of the apparitions.

My brother John received a scholarship at De La Salle. Before him, my grandfather had studied there. Let's just say it was just tradition for Eugene and me to attend, as well. We both flourished academically. We also joined any and every activity offered. John ended up in the band, too.

In addition to the cultivation of our Catholic faith, the sisters and Christian Brothers at De La Salle High School made us acutely aware of what was happening in the world. We learned that communism, fascism, and Nazism were all brothers in evil. All such regimes used whatever tools necessary to destroy the soul's natural inclination to do right and honor God. We understood that these oppressive regimes represented a perennial battle for the eternal salvation of souls. Beginning in the seventh grade, we read from a Catholic periodical that reported on national and international news. We learned of the atrocities that had taken place in the concentration camps. The Jews were the minority in Germany. It was easy for Hitler to wage a "hatred" campaign, turning them into scapegoats so that he could advance his socialistic aims. We also learned about the civil war in Spain and the torture and death of Augustinian priests. Some were buried alive with only their heads protruding from the ground. These news stories have stayed with me over a lifetime. They drove home to me that evil is real, and it is the task of every good person to resist it.

I began this chapter by pointing out that a human life unfolds within many stories already in process. At this point, then, I must say a word about the story of the Chicago area. My young life took shape in this unique part of the United States. It provided me with the narrative framework for my career and the raising of my family. At the same time, it is true to say that the Dolehide family has made its contributions to the history and culture of the area. I know for certain that there is a street named after me!

It may be hard to believe, given the size and diversity of Chicago's population today, that the city originated with the work of Catholic missionaries. In fact, the Catholic faith shaped Chicago's original identity and is still evident today despite the ravages of secularism and socialist politics. We can thank the Society of Jesus, the "Jesuits," for this fact. In the mid-1600s, the Jesuit priests Marquette and Joliet explored the area. Thirty years later, another Jesuit founded the Mission of the Guardian Angel. Of all cities in the United States, the Jesuits struck their deepest roots in Chicago.

The 1800s saw the foundation of Catholic hospitals, medical schools, and universities throughout Chicago. The mission of Catholic hospitals – so courageously begun by religious sisters – was to serve the poor of the community who were in need of medical care. In 1852, Mercy Hospital, run by the Sisters of Mercy, became the first chartered Catholic hospital to affiliate with a medical school. Loyola University of Chicago began in 1872. The Congregation of the Mission established DePaul University in 1898 to serve the needs of poor immigrants who had little opportunity for higher education in Chicago. These institutions came into being because of the Church's charitable imperative to save souls and better society.

Catholicism in Chicago has always had an ethnic dimension. By 1850, Irish Catholic immigrants accounted for about one-fifth of the city's population. The vast majority of these Irish came to the city in impoverished circumstances due to the Great Famine in Ireland. Taking low-skilled and poorly-paid jobs in brickyards, meatpacking plants, and factories, Irish immigrants settled into poor neighborhoods such as Bridgeport on the South Side or Kilglubbin on the North Side. In time, their economic status improved. Their children grew up to be better off than their parents. The Irish began moving up the social ladder, gaining positions in the workplace, especially the police and fire departments. They formed the beginnings of the trade union movements and eventually occupied political offices. Other immigrant peoples contributed to the rapid growth of Chicago: Poles, Czechs, Slovaks, Croats, and Italians. Local churches were important centers of faith and culture where the spiritual needs of these peoples could be met. The parochial schools provided instruction in the Catholic faith, along with a solid education in secular subjects. Life in the parish communities was active and vibrant. The people enjoyed a strong sense of family and community. I came on the scene at the tail end of this history. I enjoyed the benefits of a Catholic culture – and witnessed its dissolution.

The subtle breakup of Catholic culture in Chicago began in the early sixties with the advent of birth control, women's increasing participation in the labor force, and a dramatic increase in divorce rates. A fundamental change in ideas about family life and the procreation of children had a serious impact on marriages. The availability of contraceptives was partly responsible. I will return to this part of the story later in regard to medical practice.

The Church has always spoken of the need for responsible parenthood. Such responsibility starts with recognizing the nature of human sexuality and the significance of the marriage bond. According to traditional Christian beliefs, God intends sexual activity only for married couples because only in marriage can its aims be realized. These aims are the love, unity, and procreative potential of the married couple. Although these three elements can be distinguished intellectually, in reality, they are one. To separate them in any way in practice is to do violence to the conjugal act. Sex without love or unity or openness to life is an aberration – a perversion – and therefore immoral. It is a violation of God's law.

The intrinsic unity between the physical act of love and the possibility of conception gives the marriage act extraordinary dignity. It is an act to be engaged in only by those who were prepared to accept the responsibility of parenthood. Parenthood itself is seen as a blessing, not a curse. Catholics accept children as gifts from God. They embrace the work of child raising as part of a sacred vocation. Long before Vatican Council II gave official recognition to the vocation of the laity, Catholic laypeople had for centuries understood that charity really does begin at home.

Secular humanism and the socialist ideals of people like Margaret Sanger (founder of Planned Parenthood) redefined marriage and sexuality. They broke the traditional, integrated view into pieces by driving a wedge between the physical dimension of sex and its procreative potential. Even before the Pill appeared on the scene, birth control advocates preached that sex could be enjoyed for itself without any reference to a woman's fertility. In fact, it was the desire to separate sex from fertility that fueled the effort to develop the Pill.

It doesn't take a degree in sociology to understand what a radical turning point this was for culture. Once sex and fertility were sundered, the door was opened to all kinds of abuses within and without marriage. Sex without responsibility was particularly damaging to women who became objectified in an unprecedented way. We could say that the rise in domestic violence, child abuse, and pornography all have their origins in the "desacralizing" of sexuality. Is it any wonder that within a century, the Supreme

Court would sanction gay "marriage"? If heterosexual couples can be married without being open to conception, any kind of couple could claim the right to be "married." The very logic of marriage has been undone.

This long excursion into the breakdown of the family illustrates the wisdom of hindsight. I doubt many people of the time I'm describing could have predicted the dire consequences of contraception for family life. Pope Paul VI did – but he was a voice crying in the wilderness. I think there was a certain naiveté in most of us. Who could have imagined that a determined and well-considered movement was underway to undo our fundamental values? Knowing what I do now, I sometimes find it hard to look back. My memories of childhood are happy ones, despite the difficult challenges my family faced. At the same time, these happy memories concern a world that no longer exists. Joined to the wisdom of hindsight is the grief that accompanies loss.

"A voice is heard in Ramah, weeping and great mourning, Rachel weeping for her children and refusing to be comforted, because they are no more."[3]

---

[3] Jeremiah 31:15

Chapter Two

Crossroads in the Pacific

We could never learn to be brave and patient if there were only joy in the world. - Helen Keller

In 1943, I enrolled at St. Mary's University in Winona, Minnesota. I was quite the athlete in those days, climbing through windows after curfew. Whatever college shenanigans I could have got into came to an abrupt end thanks to World War II. My brother Eugene entered the Army; I settled on the Navy. After our initial induction into military life, we were sent to special military schools. I underwent training at Northwestern University Midshipman School in Chicago, followed by Japanese Interpreter School in Stillwater, Oklahoma. I then headed to the South Pacific as one of the "90-day wonders" on the fast track for military leadership.

I could not have known as the ocean miles passed under me that I was on my way to the education of a lifetime. Like many in those days, I was simply a young man doing his duty. Moreover, I was eager to play my part in what we all understood to be a global mission to end tyranny. Journalist Tom Brokaw has described Americans at this time as "the greatest generation" – and so we were. The lines between good and evil were clearly drawn back then. Extraordinary sacrifices were our daily fare as we took up the cause of free-dom and justice. An outcome of our efforts, however, was a shrinking of the world. We encountered new peoples and ways of thinking that laid the foundation for post-war culture. This fact had both good and bad consequences, as we shall see.

For my own part, the time I spent in the South Pacific was a turning point. In many ways, the young man who left Chicago for the sunny islands of the South Pacific was not the same man who came back. My experiences there challenged some of my most taken-for-granted notions; they shook me out of my youthful complacency and turned my mind to the serious and enduring concerns of an adult. In those days, I stood at a crossroads from which I chose the path I would follow the rest of my life.

"Crossroads" is an appropriate word given the geography – and the politics. The conflict with Japan had ended with the dropping of atom bombs on Hiroshima and Nagasaki. After the war, the U. S. military continued experimenting with its new, game-changing weapon. It did so at a tiny atoll not far from where I was stationed. The name given to the first of these tests was "Operation Crossroads."

Many people debate today the use of atomic bombs on Japan, as well as the atomic testing that followed. They rarely put the situation in context. At that time, the question that loomed in everyone's mind was who would have ultimate control in the world. The communist had conquest on their minds. Those who represented the free world had no alternative but to arm themselves with atomic weapons. Once both sides had nuclear capability, the race for supremacy was on. By the time I arrived in the Pacific, my country was truly at a moral crossroads. Would it continue to pursue the development of a potentially world-destroying weapon? Or would it back away, allowing other nations to move ahead with this technology and, as a result, command world destiny? The atomic testing on Bikini Atoll was the practical consequence of the first option.

But I had none of this on my mind when I landed on Kwajalein Island in May of 1943. My first priority was obeying orders. My second preoccupation was coming to terms with a new and exotic environment that bore no resemblance whatsoever to Chicago. Like many U.S. personnel stationed in the Pacific, I sometimes felt like Alice in Wonderland, navigating a fascinating world of strange logic. If you have seen the musical "South Pacific," then you know what I mean when I say that service in the South Pacific could challenge homegrown values and expectations. We were, in fact, surrounded by contradictions that were almost too much to fathom sometimes. The ravages of war everywhere marked stunning natural beauty. The simple life and wisdom of island natives crumbled in the face of modern politics and technology. And then there was the nuclear testing that made uninhabitable some of the most glorious places imaginable. Someone has said that in the South Pacific human beings found the nearest thing to paradise on earth and then turned it into hell. It was impossible to witness these things and not be changed.

I was stationed on Kwajalein Island, the southernmost and largest island of the Kwajalein Atoll. "Kwaj," as we called it, lies at the heart of the Marshall Islands, about 2000 miles southwest of Hawaii. It consists of a string of ninety-three islands that include one of the largest coral atolls on the planet. Some readers may recognize Kwajalein Island from 2014 movie "Unbroken" about the life of Olympian Louis Zamperini. During the war, Zamperini served as an army pilot flying B-24 "Liberator" bombers in the Pacific. After his plane went down, he survived for 47 days drifting on the ocean until the Japanese picked him up. He underwent six weeks of interrogation on Kwajalein, known at the time as "Execution Island." He actually did better off there than during the two years he spent as a Prisoner of War in Japan.

Kwajalein's 1,560 acres stretch 2.5 miles long by about 800 yards wide and surround one of the world's biggest lagoons. Sunk in these waters, however, are the wrecks of many warships and aircraft – the remains of a major battle. For years before the war, the area had been a trading outpost administered by Japanese civilians and worked by the natives. At the outbreak of war, the Japanese military moved onto the atoll, making it an integral part of their perimeter defense. On February 1, 1944, the United Stated subjected Kwajalein to the most concentrated bombardment of the Pacific War. Tens of thousands of shells landed on the island from every direction. The cost for the Japanese was high. 7870 of 8782 military personnel lost their lives. Many non-Japanese also died. Some were forced Korean laborers, and some were Marshallese natives convinced by Japanese propaganda that the Americans would rape and murder their people. In a rare event for the Pacific front, these natives fought for the

Japanese. With no place to hide during the invasion, the natives fled to huts that were easily destroyed by grenades.

The battle of Kwajalein ended on February 6 with an American victory. Kwajalein Atoll had strategic importance for U.S. forces in the Pacific as a natural stepping-stone to the Japanese homeland. In fact, it became a major staging area for further campaigns in the Pacific. In addition, the fall of Kwajalein represented a moral victory since the Americans had succeeded in penetrating the "outer ring" of Japanese defense. The Japanese, too, understood the significance of their defeat. The lessons they learned on Kwajalein served to tighten defenses on other islands, thereby prolonging the war.

Such was the immediate historical context when I arrived on Kwajalein Island. As a communications officer and Japanese interpreter, I served as the manager for the atoll's radio station, appropriately called WXLG, "Radio Kwajalein - Crossroads of the Pacific." The station already had quite a reputation. Shortly after the Americans had captured the island, the joint Army-Navy command established a small Welfare and Recreation office there. A call went out for anyone with broadcast experience and within a few weeks an eleven-man crew came together. The group had considerable experience among them, ranging from station management to major league baseball announcing. In June of 1944, the first radio station in the Marshall Islands went on the air. It began with a 50-watt transmitter from a local radio repair shop. Daily programs of music and news ran three times a day. Thanks to a young Army sergeant named Russell Beggs, WXLG became one of the biggest single morale boosters across much of the

South Pacific. Beggs gave a humorous slant to the daily grind of military routing of the bases at Kwaj and Roi-Namur. By February 1945, WXLG could boast a 500-watt transmitter broadcasting a thirteen-hour, seven- day schedule. Oddly enough, the designation "Operation Crossroads" for the atomic tests at Bikini Atoll came from fans of the station among Admiral Blandy's staff.

Officially, WXLG existed to serve the interests of the U.S. military in the Pacific. A sign painted by the U.S. Seabees hung on the front of the Quonset hut: "WXLG Armed Forces Radio Network." In reality, our programs were a mixed bag. Weekly, we broadcast a live amateur hour from the island's Richardson Theater stage. There was also a daily chaplain's hour, interviews with entertainers from passing USO shows, and prerecorded programs from favorites like Charlie McCarthy, Edgar Bergen, Jack Benny, and Bob Hope.

From the beginning, the station had also broadcast live or recorded music of Marshallese natives. As manager of the station, I was happy to welcome a group of natives wishing to sing their religious hymns. They were a very happy bunch. Freed from the yolk of the godless Japanese, they were once again able to practice and express their centuries-old Christian heritage. They came to me with a script in hand. After being introduced to the radio audience, they sang without any musical accompaniment. Dressed in armed forces fatigues, native men, women, and children would cluster together in the station's huge Quonset hut lined with acoustic tile. A tribal leader, Paul, and his council oversaw the natives, whose home consisted of a colony of small huts and coconut plantations.

Paul would come in daily to the station to tell me how happy the natives on the surrounding islands were to once again hear religious and native songs, as well as news of local import.

The war in the Pacific had been over about six months when word reached us that the United States was preparing to test an atomic bomb on nearby Bikini Atoll, 225 miles northwest of Kwajalein. This would be just the beginning. From 1946 to 1962, the United States used locations around the Marshall Islands as the so-called "pacific proving grounds" to test nuclear bombs.[4] The first twenty-three detonations took place at Bikini Atoll.

Few people today realize the extent of nuclear testing in the South Pacific. In sum, 105 atmospheric (as opposed to underground) tests took place in the Marshall Islands. The largest of these – and one of the world's first nuclear accidents – was the "Castle Bravo" test. Expected to yield 4 or 5 megatons, this first hydrogen bomb yielded 15 megatons and spread nuclear fallout   over many nearby islands, some of them inhabited. To this day, people on these islands continue to suffer the effects of radiation poisoning. In 1990, $759 million was paid to Marshall Islanders in compensation. In 1963, the Partial Test Ban Treaty put an end to atmospheric and underwater nuclear tests. Henceforth, testing would be done underground or in space.

---

[4] The United Nations created the "Trust Territory of the Pacific Islands" as a strategic trusteeship territory under the control of the United States. The Trust Territory consisted of 2,000 islands spread over three million square miles.

Operation Crossroads meant new responsibilities for us on Kwaj. Although it hadn't been part of the plan, natives relocated from testing sites ended up on our atoll. Suddenly, we had our hands full, housing and then further relocating a people who had already been jostled about more than expected. The story is one of the most tragic of the post-war South Pacific.

Prior to the atomic tests, the U.S. military arranged for the 167 natives of Bikini Atoll to be relocated to islands considered a safe distance from nuclear fallout.[5] In February 1946, Navy Commodore Ben H. Wyatt, the military governor of the Marshall Islands, traveled to Bikini Atoll. On a Sunday, after church, he assembled the natives to ask if they would be willing to leave their home temporarily so that the United States could test atomic bombs for what he called "the good of mankind and to end all world wars." The governor promised that the natives would be able to return to the atoll after a short time. After much confused and sorrowful deliberation among the natives, the leader of the Bikini people stood up and announced their decision: "We will go, believing that everything is in the hands of God."

Sadly, the promise of a quick return to Bikini Atoll was not fulfilled. The devastation to the atoll was so great – particularly after the Castle Bravo test – that to this day no one can linger there for very long. But the suffering of the Bikini people had only just begun. Rongerik Atoll, the place to which

---

[5] A brief history of the Bikini Atoll people is available at http://www.bikiniatoll.com/history.html.

the natives were first relocated, could not provide enough food and drinking water for the people. They starved. The military relocated them again, this time to Kwajalein Atoll where they lingered in limbo for six months until finally landing on Kili Island – a place one-sixth the size of their original home. Here, too, food production was inadequate for the needs of the people. Eventually, the Bikinis scattered to other islands and remain so to this day. [6]

I remember well the expanding population of Marshallese natives on Kwaj. It fell to me to assist in their relocation to more permanent situations. From both practical and humanitarian points of view, this was not an easy task. I felt deeply the plight of these people. I also wondered at their readiness to accept the total evacuation of their atoll. I asked Paul about it, and he explained that the natives believed the United States was their friend. The Americans had saved them from Japanese dictatorship and restored their freedom, especially their religious freedom. You won't find it in the history books, but the willingness of the Bikinis to relocate had a lot to do with their gratitude for being able to live as Christians.

In the middle of native relocations, I also had to oversee a daily radio broadcast. As the dreaded testing day approached, a complement of five sailors helped me keep the 500-watt station beaming local and international news to

---

[6] Some natives returned to Bikini Island in 1970. Testing later, however, revealed dangerous levels of strontium-90; hence, the islanders were moved again. They continue to receive compensation from trust funds established by the United States government.

ships' personnel from Guam in the north to the coast of New Zealand in the south. All of this depended, of course, on the cooperation of the weather.

Although we were not close enough on Kwaj to see any indications of the atomic tests, we were all aware that they were happening. The world has become very complacent now about nuclear arms. Perhaps we are just used to living with them. This was not the case in 1947. We had all seen the news reels that had come out of Hiroshima and Nagasaki. From these indelible images, we understood that the atom bomb was a destructive power like no other. A strange mixture of fear and awe was upon us all.

As the day drew near, I wondered when news of the first test would come over the teletype. When it did, I noticed a certain "poetic license" in the information. This was my first experience of a manipulation of facts by the Associated Press. Years later, I had even more reason to question their veracity. At that time, I was a novice – naïve and eager to fulfill the tasks given to me. I obediently relayed the information I received in its entirety on the air.

Another memory of my time on Kwajalein remains very strong. We had Japanese POWS on the atoll. To put this in perspective, you have to consider what the Japanese meant to us Americans in those days. Perhaps we could draw an analogy with the way people might feel about Muslims today. There was an element of curiosity . . . and fear. As we understood it, the Japanese had attacked us at Pearl Harbor with no warning. They had gone on to perpetrate horrible war crimes. We heard stories about the things they had done to

captured U.S. servicemen and women. I admit that I felt
unsettled by the presence of Japanese on the island. I don't
know whether it was curiosity or a desire to reach out, but I
made a visit to one Japanese naval officer – my first personal
contact with the enemy. It struck me that neither he nor I could
conceive why God would plan this meeting. I felt sorry for
him, knowing that his code of honor frowned on his being
captured by the enemy. It would have been more dignified for
him to die in battle. He did not care to converse with me. His
sense of dishonor and fear was palpable. After bowing, he
simply turned around and walked back to his quarters.

This encounter made me think long and hard about war
and what constitutes a "just" war. Pope Pius XII wrote:

> Every war of aggression is a sin, a crime, an
> outrage against the majesty of God, Creator and
> Governor of the world. A people threatened with
> unjust aggression, and already its victim,
> however, may not remain passively indifferent if
> it would think and act in a Christian way. And the
> solidarity of nations does not permit other nations
> to behave as mere spectators with an attitude of
> apathetic neutrality.[7]

As an American, I believed that my country had a role to fulfill
in the world as a defender of justice and right. The words of
Woodrow Wilson concerning America's entry into World

---

[7] Pope Pius XII, "Christmas Message of 1948," Vincent A Yzermans,
ed., *The Major Addresses of Pope Pius XII* (St. Paul: The North Central
Publishing Company, 1961), Vol. 2, p. 124.

War I expressed our courageous stance among the nations of
the world:

> It is a fearful thing to lead this great peaceful
> people into war, into the most terrible and
> disastrous of all wars, civilization itself seeming
> to be in the balance. But the right is more
> precious than peace, and we shall fight for the
> things which we have always carried nearest our
> hearts—for democracy, for the right of those who
> submit to authority to have a voice in their own
> governments, for the rights and liberties of small
> nations, for a universal dominion of right by such
> a concert of free peoples as shall bring peace and
> safety to all nations and make the world itself at
> last free.[8]

At this point in my life, my patriotism embraced what I
believed were the fundamental values of my country: respect
for human life and love for justice. Granted, as a nation, we
did not always behave in accord with these ideals, but they
were, nonetheless, the bedrock of our political and social life.

It is only in hindsight sometimes that we understand
the true significance of events. At the time, life at the
Kwajalein base consisted mostly of fulfilling my military duty
every day. I had a job to do, and I did it to the best of my
ability. Looking back now, however, I realize that many

---

[8] On April 2, 1917, President Woodrow Wilson went before a joint
session of Congress to seek a Declaration of War against Germany.
Available at http://historymatters.gmu.edu/d/4943/.

influences came together during that time to further my growth as a human being and sharpen the values that would remain for a lifetime. Being far from my country and a witness to the values of other peoples, I became conscious of the greatness of the national heritage I had received. My Christian faith deepened, as well, becoming truly Catholic – a word that means "universal." Having seen great suffering, I looked with new eyes at the crucifix. Jesus had said to his mother from the cross, "Behold your son." The Church Fathers took this to mean that we are to see the suffering Christ in every suffering person.

My vocation to medicine also awakened during this period. Young men seek to emulate the virtues they see in older men. I was no exception. During my time on Kwaj, I shared quarters with four Navy physicians. These men impressed me deeply with their dedication as doctors, as well as their kindness and consideration toward the native population. It has been said that we can be part of the problem or part of the solution. Amid the ashes of war and the shadow of greater evils to come, these men inspired me with a desire to be part of the solution. I wanted to care for the sick with the same kind of dedication and welcoming spirit that I had seen in them.

Of course, as a single Catholic male, I had to consider one other possibility. I wondered if I should follow my brother John into the seminary and embrace a life of total subjugation to authority with perpetual vows of poverty, chastity, and obedience. The good sisters who had educated me had always taught that the most rewarding life was one given totally to

God in the priesthood or religious vocation. I had to take a long, hard look at myself and ask if I had the call. I decided I didn't. The married life appealed to me too much. And that was okay. We had also learned that the married vocation was holy, too, if pursued without self-seeking.

Hence, upon my return to the United States, I decided to pursue my interest in medicine and lay the foundation of a career that would support a family. I believed that the souls and well- being of the people of Chicago were just as important as the natives in the South Pacific, and probably at a greater disadvantage considering the materialism that began to rule in my country. Little could I imagine how much materialism would lay claim to our society in the years ahead. Nor could I have known that the worldwide conflict that had marked "the greatest generation" did not end in peace and justice for all. In truth, World War II turned out to be a crossroads between traditional values and a New World order. The forces of right had won the battle on the ground, but the spiritual battle would continue for some time to come.

Chapter Three

A Culture of Life and Learning

The human person . . . is and ought to be the principle, the subject and the end of all social institutions. - Gaudium et Spes

Few today will remember the exuberance of the years following World War II. As a nation, we were bent on building a new world, a better world, one that would not end up in the horrors some of us had witnessed firsthand in Europe and the Pacific. Those who returned from military service sought the good things of this life: family, security, and social harmony. Our experiences had prepared us to do well. We had discipline, training, and the bond of common values. We also had the confidence of victors, having met and triumphed over formidable foes. We were the good guys who had saved the world from the evil designs of totalitarian regimes.

On the surface, and for a while, the familiar trappings of America's pre-war culture ruled. Little by little, however, a new and unfamiliar culture began to manifest itself. In the next chapter, I will describe the impact of this new culture on the medical profession. Here, I wish to pay homage to the twilight of what has been called "a culture of life." For me, this culture existed in microcosm at Chicago's Cook County

Hospital where I did my internship. I was fortunate to learn my profession at a time and in a place that cherished the values embodied in the Hippocratic Oath.

As it turned out, the transition from Navy to civilian life was more difficult than I had expected. Part of this, no doubt, was due to the change in personal perspective that I described in the last chapter. As the Gospel teaches, you can't put new wine into old wine skins. The "new skin" for me was the life of a medical student and then intern. Although I had longed to come home to what was familiar and comfortable, I soon found myself plunged into a new world as challenging as anything I had experienced overseas.

My situation was not unique. Many returning veterans opted for study and professional development. The men who had enlisted as teenagers came home after the war as adults. Many had been places and had seen things beyond anything they could have ever imagined. A grateful nation was ready to thank them for their service. One such expression was the passing of the 1944 G. I. Bill of Rights that provided returning World War II veterans with funds for medical care, unemployment insurance, higher education, and housing. Millions of veterans who would have flooded the job market chose instead to go to school. The transition to a daily regimen of study was not as easy as it sounds. The same individuals who had led men into battle, commanded powerful war ships, and flown dangerous missions sometimes felt weak in the knees in front of papers and exams. This was a new kind of battle that required a new kind of resolution. Some were able to meet this challenge, and some fell by the wayside. By the grace of God, I was able to succeed and move forward.

I wasn't the only one putting on a new skin at this time. My home city was undergoing a radical transformation. Inundated with returning veterans and European refugees, it enjoyed an economic and population boom. FHA loans stimulated housing development and provided a way for families to get ahead. The Northwest and Southwest sides of Chicago experienced a frenzy of construction. Many new businesses popped up. Within a short time, parts of the city were all but unrecognizable.

What a different America we had then! Today, our economy is gasping for breath while families struggle to make ends meet. People put off marriage and family, sometimes for years, because they cannot afford either. In the period I am describing, America was full of confidence and hope. Jobs were plentiful. Every family seemed to be having babies – the famous "Baby Boomers." The dream of the day was a house in the suburbs, close to church and school, inhabited by children and material possessions, surrounded by a yard, in a neighborhood with curbs, streets, and water hydrants, where people could work hard and respect the ways of others, where families could get along on their own and come together for recreation and leisure. Houses popped up, and the birthrate soared, and Chicago families settled into the Southwest side and the neighboring suburbs. Life was good.

My first move upon returning stateside was to pick up where I had left off in my education. As an undergraduate at St. Mary's College, I had taken mostly pre-medical courses.

These were enough to get me accepted into the Stritch School of Medicine at Loyola University in 1947. Four years later, I joined Cook County Hospital as a full-fledged intern. The institution's history is entwined with that of the city. Since this history was the backdrop of my formative years as a physician, it's apropos to consider it for a moment.

Back in the day when Chicago was under Northwest Territory law, the Illinois General Assembly assigned the care of the poor to local counties. From 1832 to 1866, Cook County provided food and medicine in makeshift hospitals and private dwellings. At that time, doctors and interns from Rush Medical School worked as volunteers. In 1857, the city of Chicago erected a permanent hospital. After serving as an army hospital during the Civil War, this structure was traded for 160 acres and an old reform school, a brick and limestone building remembered today as "Old County Hospital." In its time, Old County was said to have the most modern equipment: knives, saws, and chisels for autopsies!

Right from the start, Cook County was a teaching hospital. Neither physicians nor their interns were paid. All were volunteers. Although life for the interns was difficult, it also provided them with enormous amounts of practical experience. Hence, Cook County was a win/win for the whole community. The poor received competent medical care, and medical students got hands on experience.

Given its mission to serve the poor, Cook County welcomed many newcomers to the United States over the years, earning for itself the nickname "Chicago's Statue of Liberty." In the early years of the 20th century, most immigrants were from Europe. Between the two world wars, however, the demographic at the hospital changed with African-American migration from the south exceeding that from across the Atlantic. In fact, until the civil rights movement, Cook County Hospital was one of only a handful of hospitals in the Chicago area open to African-American patients.

The founding ideals of Cook County Hospital, noble as they were, did not save it from Chicago's infamous political corruption. Cut backs and pay offs led to the deterioration of the hospital building. Crowding became an issue as the city's population increased throughout the 1870s. Eventually, at the insistence of the medical community, the city erected a new 300-bed facility between Harrison, Polk, Lincoln, and Wood Streets. Instead of a happy ending, however, ongoing mismanagement resulted in a walkout of medical staff and the hiring of incompetent replacements.

Things started looking up for Cook County Hospital with the arrival of Danish physician Christian Fenger. A noted surgeon, scientist, and teacher, Fenger brought a new level of professionalism to Cook County Hospital. The greatest fruit of his work, however, were his interns, some of whom rose to national prominence. Another step forward for the hospital was   the appearance of board exams in the early 1900s. These exams led to improved patient care at all hospitals in Chicago. Through the 1920s and 1930s, Cook County continued to expand its services and reputation. During World War II, a lack of nurses precipitated a crisis; after the war, the need to update facilities became painfully evident. Progress was difficult, however, thanks to internal conflicts. By the 1960s, full-time, paid physicians had replaced volunteer work. This new wave of young, ambitious personnel took on the "old guard" and demanded radical changes. By 1979 the hospital was fully in the hands of the County Board of Commissioners.

No matter its complicated history, Cook County's founding mission to serve the poor remained a constant. One can only marvel at the heroic efforts that went in to realizing this mission. The hospital faced chronic funding crises, supply shortages, and terrible overcrowding. It is a testimony to the dedication and skills of the hospital's staff that they not only managed to care for patients under these circumstances, but also advance the frontiers of medicine again and again.

At the time I showed up, Cook County was a 4,500-bed hospital surrounded by six medical schools, as well as a medical building, surgical building, psychiatric building, and an infectious disease hospital. Patients were admitted for leprosy, pernicious anemia, tuberculosis, malaria, and myxedema. A large population suffered from syphilitic heart disease, arthritis, leukemia, lupus, bowel cancer, and stab and bullet wounds. The 1950s was the decade when degenerative pathologies started superseding infectious diseases as the major cause of chronic health issues in the United States. Affluence had come to Chicago, and with it, a hedonistic lifestyle. Even the poor were smoking, drinking, and eating too much. Tuberculosis, pneumonia, and malnutrition gradually gave way to cirrhosis of the liver, lung cancer, emphysema, and coronary occlusive disease.

For us interns, Cook County Hospital was trial by fire. In my first two weeks, I had a revolving call cycle of 12 hours on and 12 hours off. The salary was $7.50 a month with room and board. Air conditioning could be had by opening a window. The Irish waitress in the cafeteria treated us well. I suppose she knew how hard we were working and how little we were being paid. In any case, we kept our complaints to ourselves and focused on our development as doctors. With over 800 interns and a revolving door of every imaginable medical condition, Cook County Hospital offered an unparalleled exchange of information and knowledge.

Each ward on the surgical service had approximately fifty patients for each intern, with four to six new admissions a day. We worked in surgery all morning, only to arrive in the ward to discover more patients who had just been admitted from the emergency room. Stab wounds, gunshot wounds, and people bleeding from other orifices always had us on particular alert. I spent most of my time as an intern delivering babies, primarily to black mothers. It was a great pleasure to deliver new life – occasionally twins – to these happy women. The hospital's frequent shortage of nurses and other medical personnel meant we interns often wore many hats. We helped review labs, perform medical procedures, and coordinate patient care. We also continued to attend lectures. Our motto was, "See one, do one, teach one." When not on duty, we would hit the books to prepare for rotations and licensure exams. There was never a dull moment. When our three-month service in an area came to a close, we methodically explained to our replacements every detail (which could be quite lengthy) concerning our charges. No attending physician, but only the resident doctor, could legally assume this responsibility.

In my time at Cook County Hospital, both the Democratic and Republican parties controlled the board. In general, this shared responsibility worked well. Dr. Karl Meyer served as Medical Director from 1930 until approximately 1960. He was loved and revered by all hospital personnel – and for good reason. Dr. Meyer was a model administrator. He demanded attention to duty from all of us. At the same time, we had no reason to fear him as long as we were forthright and not self-seeking.

As busy as life was in those days, I still had time for deeper reflection on what I was living. My Catholic faith was never far from my mind as I bore daily witness to the effects of original sin and the power of divine grace. Many times, I wondered how non-believing doctors approached their work and patients, especially in regard to terminal illness. I was struck by an apparent contradiction in many of my colleagues. They would brag about their atheism, but show the greatest respect and devotion to their patients' personal beliefs in an immortal soul. I often observed the deference they showed to the priests ministering to our patients. We worked side by side with Franciscan clerics in their brown robes and sandaled feet. My non-believing colleagues would discreetly step aside to allow a minister to care for the soul of a patient. I marveled at such humility and acceptance of another person's beliefs. I also wondered how someone without faith understood and coped with the suffering we saw on a daily basis. I still wonder to this day.

Although internship meant dealing with a host of different medical conditions, there were some pathologies at Cook County Hospital that received more attention than others. The Pernicious Anemia Clinic, for example, had a complement of four hundred patients suffering from closely related irreversible neurological complications because of posterolateral spinal cord disease, as well as severe anemia. The most virulent of these diseases was named pernicious anemia because it was almost always fatal without proper treatment. The disease concerns a protein called "intrinsic factor" (IF). Released by the stomach, IF helps the intestines absorb vitamin B12, which is found naturally in food. Sufferers of pernicious anemia do not release enough IF, with the result that the intestines cannot properly absorb vitamin B12. The disease develops rapidly and can irreparably impair the bone marrow and spinal cord.

Today, it is fairly easy to diagnose pernicious anemia. This was not the case during my internship. The procedure was long and complicated. We were trained to perform a sternal bone marrow aspiration. We would then stain the material extracted and microscopically examine it to determine the presence of anemia. Most importantly, we needed to be sure that we were not looking at the early stages of leukemia or congenital lipid disorder. If the test results confirmed pernicious anemia, treatment had to be swift. Unfortunately, at the time, the hospital did not have B12 solution; researchers were still working on a cure for the disease. Instead, patients received weekly intravenous injections of liver extract obtained from the Chicago stockyards. Occasionally, they needed blood transfusions, too.

I didn't realize it then, but I was doing my internship in a hospital at the cutting edge of many major breakthroughs in health care. There is no room here to tell the full story of Cook County Hospital. I would like to dwell briefly on some of the cases and individuals who in one way or another had an impact on my time there.

One name looms larger than most in the annals of Cook County Hospital: Dr. Herman Bundesen. Chicago owes a great deal to this colorful character who authored a classic text on baby care – "Dr. Bundesen's Baby Book" – and served as coroner after the infamous St. Valentine's Day massacre. In his 34 years as the city's health commissioner, Bundesen implemented health care programs that reached far beyond Chicago.

One of Bundesen's most significant breakthroughs concerned thyroid endocrinology. Patients would show up at the hospital with bulging eyes and large masses in their thyroid glands. Their necks were oversized and they had difficulty swallowing and breathing. Bundesen discovered that the iodine levels in Lake Michigan water were very low. Thanks to his research and persistence, a law went into effect requiring all salt and salt tablets to be iodized. Within ten years, thyroid enlargement cases decreased significantly.

I remember well the time I spent at Cook County Hospital diagnosing cases of thyroid dysfunction. Our procedure was based on the operations of the thyroid hormones T3 and T4. In the absence of adequate amounts of these hormones, or in cases where the action of these hormones is blocked, patients can experience an entire cascade of neurotransmitter abnormalities that may lead to mood and personality changes. The thyroid is co-involved in emotions such as joy, panic, anger, fear, and anxiety. Patients suffering from undiagnosed thyroid dysfunction very often ended up at the psychiatric hospital where they were treated for depression, mania, or other psychiatric disorders. To identity thyroid dysfunction, we used good clinical judgment along with a basil metabolism machine for accuracy. We observed patients for pulse, skin texture, and behavior. And when we were done with them, they went to the medical ward for further evaluation. This tedious process is now non-existent because blood levels can be tested accurately now for level of thyroid hormones.

Before moving on, I should mention another of Bundesen's efforts since it will tie in later with the change in medical culture. Bundesen rose to national fame thanks to his revolutionary treatment and prevention of venereal disease. During World War I, syphilis was a huge problem among military personnel. To limit the spread of the disease, infected individuals were imprisoned. After the war, Bundesen spearheaded the fight against syphilis and other venereal diseases by distributing condoms in brothels, restrooms, pharmacies, and clinics. He took a lot of heat for his efforts. Many people accused him of promoting immorality. But Bundesen didn't quit, and by 1937 he obtained national funding for a comprehensive public health campaign against syphilis. For the most part, Bundesen was successful in his campaign against syphilis, but there is no doubting that the introduction of prophylactics into the mainstream led to the normalization of their use as contraception.

Another memory from my Cook County Hospital days concerns the outbreak and subsequent suppression of poliomyelitis. Few people today truly understand the meaning of the word "epidemic." Once in a while, the public gets a scare from something like swine flu or Legionnaires Disease. My generation lived through a real and terrifying epidemic: polio. This drama played out while I was at Cook County Hospital. In fact, my internship class was the last to witness and treat polio on a grand scale.

Polio was not a new pathology. Local epidemics of the disease had appeared in Europe and the United States around the turn of the century. During the first half of the 20th century, however, these numbers skyrocketed to pandemic proportions. At first, the greatest number of cases was infants. By 1950, however, children aged five to nine years old were more often struck by the disease. One third of the cases reported were people over the age of fifteen. The worst outbreak in U.S. history occurred in 1952. Of the nearly 58,000 cases reported that year, over 3,000 people died and 21, 269 suffered simple to grave paralysis. What we know today as "intensive care" came into being during this time to help patients who had lost their capacity to breathe. These people were placed in "iron lungs," long cylindrical tubes that could breathe for them.

Thanks to Jonas Salk's vaccine, polio eventually lost its grip on the world. I wonder, though, if our triumph over this and other diseases contributed to the illusory belief that medicine can cure all ills. Pride is the root of all evil. A world freed from the fear of uncontrollable, infectious disease was likely to forget the fragility and preciousness of life. Perhaps the death-dealing ways of doctors today have their origins in medical breakthroughs that made them feel in control of human destiny. God gives life and takes it back. Some doctors today seem to think they can do the same thing.

In addition to advances in the treatment of pathologies, Cook County Hospital also presided over groundbreaking surgical procedures. Medical history was written and re-written within its walls. I was privileged to stand alongside some of the best surgeons in the country as they practiced their art. One thing I learned during this time was that credentials do not make a great surgeon. Some of our most skilled surgeons received little publicity, while others of repute often showed poor clinical judgment and carelessness at the operating table. In medicine, the proof of expertise is in the doing, not hanging on the wall.

Looking back, I can honestly say that Cook County Hospital provided a culture of life for everyone who came through its doors. With all of its ups and downs, it remained faithful to its mission. It provided the poor with skilled medical care. It allowed interns like me to cut their teeth on their chosen profession. I am proud of the time I spent at Cook County Hospital and grateful to have played some part in its history.

Even so, I realize now that the stirrings of a new and distorted medical culture had already begun. Small, radical, and very dedicated cliques of self-seekers focused on change for change's sake. Their aim was not to improve the health of the community through judicial and medical reform, but to attack and discredit individuals and ultimately bend things toward their own selfish ends. Every business, factory, political party or government depends on the good will of its members to succeed and make its contribution. When hatred is sown, the noble ends of an organization are derailed and impure motives manifest themselves. Change may be in order at times, but the end never justifies the means.

I could not have imagined during my internship that within eighteen years, the slaughter of unborn babies would take place at Cook County Hospital. Shortly after the U.S. Supreme Court legalized abortion in 1973, the hospital began offering abortions and quickly became an important abortion provider for low-income women in the Chicago area. I realize now, however, that abortion did not appear out of nowhere. A cultural change gradually invaded the medical profession and its institutions, not just in Chicago, but all round the country. This cultural shift worked through our legal system to redefine morality and the value of human life. Rather than resist this new vision, the majority of medical professionals jumped on board, enamored of the power and profit to be made, little regarding the inevitable consequences.

The prophetic words of St. Pope John Paul II sum up the path that the medical profession followed in the years following my internship:

"Choices once unanimously considered criminal and rejected by the common moral sense are gradually becoming socially acceptable. Even certain sectors of the medical profession, which by its calling is directed to the defense and care of human life, are increasingly willing to carry out these acts against the person. In this way the very nature of the medical profession is distorted and contradicted, and the dignity of those who practice it is degraded. In such a cultural and legislative situation, the serious demographic, social and family problems which weigh upon many of the world's peoples and which require responsible and effective attention from national and international bodies, are left open to false and deceptive solutions, opposed to the truth and the good of persons and nations.

The end result of this is tragic: not only is the fact of the destruction of so many human lives still to be born or in their final stage extremely grave and disturbing, but no less grave and disturbing is the fact that conscience itself, darkened as it were by such widespread conditioning, is finding it increasingly difficult to distinguish between good and evil in what concerns the basic value of human life."[9]

---

[9] John Paul II, *Evangelium Vitae*, 25 March 1995, #4. Available at http://w2.vatican.va/content/john-paul-ii/en/encyclicals/documents/hf_jp-ii_enc_25031995_evangelium-vitae.html.

Chapter Four

Serving a Culture of Life

*The moral test of a society is how that society
treats those who are in the dawn of life – the
children; those who are in the twilight of life –
the elderly; and those who are in the shadow of
life – the sick, the needy, and the handicapped–
Hubert H. Humphrey*

In 1955, I began as an internist/hematologist at Cook
County Hospital. My day began at 6:00am and ended at
midnight. I had little time to read. No matter. Life itself was a
daily education. The inescapable truths of the human
condition were always before me. I was often struck by the
apparent contradiction of our lives. We live in two worlds. On
the one hand, we experience pain and tragedy; on the other
hand, we know joy and fulfillment.

The question is how these two worlds can exist at the
same time. There is no easy answer. The closest I can come is
that freedom creates the possibility for both conditions. In the
Garden of Eden, a free choice to disobey God's command
brought suffering and death into the world. Much later, the
free choice of God's son to obey his Father won us eternal
salvation. True love cannot exist without freedom. God did
not want puppets who loved him on command. He wanted

rational, free beings who could know him and choose him by observing the order he put into creation. Every person who reaches the age of reason has the possibility of making this choice. Why did God make us? In the words of the Baltimore Catechism, "to know Him, to love Him, and to serve Him in this world, and to be happy with Him forever in heaven."[10]

Cook County Hospital's emergency room was a daily reminder of the tragedy and joy of human life – joy for those who were treated and dismissed, and tragedy for those who conditions required admission. In one small space, I had ample opportunity to learn the whole truth about sin and grace. I witnessed the human journey through this life to the next, even as I made my own way to that final destination. Those who confront pain and death every day must come to terms with what they experience or they will fall into depression and bitter resentment. My faith gave me a way to penetrate the veil of sorrow and keep my eye on the prize of heaven. In the midst of sorrow, I clung to the hope of eternal joy.

Joy in this life arrived the day my roommate introduced me to a former Little Company of Mary nurse named Eileen Carroll. At the time we met, Eileen was working at the University of Chicago and, in many ways, was in a better position than I was. I had no car and barely two coins to rub together. We would meet at "Greeks" restaurant across the street from the hospital for a hamburger, and then she would drive home alone. Eileen's father let her use his car to visit me, but made her take public transportation to the University

---

[10] Available at: http://www.sacredtexts.com/chr/balt/balt1.htm.

of Chicago – his way of making clear his disapproval of the university's philosophy. On October 11, 1952, as my residency was drawing to a close, Eileen and I were married. Thus began what my friend and colleague Dr. Eugene Diamond described as "a match made in heaven since they shared the Catholic ideals of parenthood and devotion to family life."

Eileen and I settled into a small apartment just two blocks from Cook County Hospital. With a salary of $15.00/month from the hospital and Eileen's contribution of $200/month, we were able to make ends meet until our first child, Robert, was born on May 19, 1954. The good sisters had always taught us that God would provide. Indeed, he did. We moved into a smaller apartment and found a way to make it all work. We've been making it work ever since.

I remember one incident during this period that impressed me with the mysterious ways of Divine Providence. I was doing an autopsy on a pretty young woman who had just delivered her second child. Though her family urgently needed her, she had been struck down by polio. In the midst of my own happiness, I found it hard to understand why this woman had been called away from this life. Why did I get to enjoy my family, and she did not? In such moments, you have to decide who knows best – you or God. Who was I to question the wisdom of the Creator who gave order and beauty to the universe?

It was my habit in those days to make daily visits to the seventh floor chapel. I needed a moment of repose in the midst of a turbulent day. During my visit that evening, still thinking of the young mother and her family, I heard the arrival of a string of ambulances. I rushed into the emergency room to offer my help and learned of a horrific traffic accident that would be remembered as one of the worst in Chicago's history.

For a few days, spring rains had fallen hard on the city. Flooding on State Street had detoured southbound trolleys to a turnaround circle that made 63rd Street a temporary last stop. On May 25th, at rush hour, the driver of a brand new, Green Hornet trolley, apparently unaware of the re-routing, made a fatal mistake. To begin with, he was driving 35 mph – much too fast. A flagman frantically tried to warn him to slow down for the switch in the track, but to no avail. The speeding trolley jumped the track and headed into traffic, smashing head on into a semi-trailer truck hauling 8,000 gallons of gasoline for local stations. The collision tore open the truck's tank in a shower of sparks that immediately ignited the gasoline. The subsequent explosion consumed both vehicles and their occupants. Being the end of the workday, the trolley was full of homebound passengers. Those who survived the initial blast vainly tried to force open side doors to escape. Steel-barred windows prevented them from exiting. Amazingly, thirty people were able to get out, leaving thirty-three others behind. The blast shook the entire neighborhood and sent flames two stories into the sky. Fire spread over seven buildings on State Street. It melted metal, fused windows, and dissolved the asphalt on the street. More than thirty fire stations reported for duty at the scene that was watched by over 20,000 spectators. A temporary morgue was set up on the street, although in some cases there was little left of a victim to gather up.

Many of the dead were taken to Cook County Hospital. At the sight of the charred and twisted bodies, I couldn't help but think of the catechism's lessons on the fires of hell. The Catholic Church has always taught that eternal punishment awaits those who disobey God's law and die impenitent. Scripture speaks of the "fires of Gehenna" that afflict souls as though they are still in the body. Many saints and mystics over the centuries have spoken about the punishment awaiting the damned. In 1935, St. Faustina Kowalska described in her diary a vision of these torments:

> I, Sister Faustina Kowalska, by the order of God, have visited the Abysses of Hell so that I might tell souls about it and testify to its existence...the devils were full of hatred for me, but they had to obey me at the command of God . . .

> Today, an angel led me to the Chasms of Hell. It is a place of great torture; how awesomely large and extensive it is! The kinds of tortures I saw: The first torture that constitutes hell is the loss of God. The second is perpetual remorse of conscious. The third is that one's condition will never change. The fourth is the fire that will penetrate the soul without destroying it. A terrible suffering since it is a purely spiritual fire, lit by God's anger. The fifth torture is continual darkness and a terrible suffocating smell, and

> despite the darkness, the devils and the souls of
> the damned see each other and all the evil, both
> of others and their own. The sixth torture is the
> constant company of Satan. The seventh torture
> is horrible despair, hatred of God, vile words,
> curses and blasphemies.[11]

Looking at the remains before me on that dreadful day in
Chicago, I wondered how anyone could worry about worldly
success and the acquisition of material goods when the loss of
heaven would mean the pains of hell. This is not to say that
any of those victims were damned. God alone knows the fate
of those souls. What I saw that day pertained to my own
spiritual condition. I understood in no uncertain terms that this
brief life brings us to one end or another. We will spend
eternity in the joy of the beatific vision, or the miseries of
Satan's infernal kingdom.

Today, priests rarely speak of the battle between the
principalities and the powers. St. Paul is very clear about it.
Prior to the liturgical changes that followed Vatican Council
II, Catholics were reminded of this drama at every Mass. The
prayers at the foot of the altar included one to St. Michael the
Archangel, the great champion of God's angels who,
according to scripture, quelled Satan's rebellion. Through the
intercession of St. Michael, we prayed: "Protect us, O Lord,
from the snare of the devil who roams through the world
seeking the ruin of souls. Thrust into hell Satan and the other
evil spirits."

---

[11] Diary 741.

The streetcar accident, like many other tragedies I have witnessed over the years, did not weaken my faith or move me to doubt the existence of a good and provident God. Today, suffering and scandal drive people away from religious belief. For my part, such evils are proof that the Catholic Church teaches truth. The articles of faith are profoundly realistic, devoid of "wishful" thinking about the human condition. Of all the religions in the world, only Catholicism offers a clear and coherent explanation for the existence of suffering and death. Only Catholicism offers a certain path for redemption.

I know many in the medical profession who have lost their faith because of what they have seen at work. I wonder sometimes if it's a matter of how you have been taught. Where is faith strongest? It is the strongest in the poorest countries where believers face harsh living conditions and insurmountable poverty. Where is it weakest? It is the weakest in wealthy nations were people, for the most part, live comfortably. Americans seems particularly vulnerable to the tragedies of this life. They are quick to blame God when bad things happen to good people. In fact, many Christian evangelists in this country make it seem that Christians will profit materially and enjoy health and security – and if they don't, they do not truly believe. Money and religion are strangely mixed in this county. There is another tendency here to see God as either the cause or disinterested spectator of human suffering. God is the ultimate villain who owes *us* an explanation.

When we struggle with such questions, we need to stand on a firm foundation of faith. Faith tells us that God is never at fault. When tragedies happen (and they will), they are not God's fault. We live in a fallen universe where sin has corrupted every level of existence. God is no more to blame when tragedy strikes than He was when the first sin infected creation. God gave human beings freedom. They abused their freedom and brought suffering and death into the world. This was surely not God's fault. Human beings must humbly accept human responsibility for the evils besetting them.

Genuine Christianity embraces both the cross and the resurrection. In this life, we know mostly the cross. Only faith keeps alive in us the hope of resurrection. As far as this world goes, Christians have no magic formula. They experience the same problems as those who do not follow Christ. Those who have faith, however, are consoled by the knowledge that God is savior as well as creator. Those without faith find life to be as Shakespeare's Macbeth described it, "a sound and fury signifying nothing." The struggle with meaningless suffering inevitably leads to despair. And despair leads to behaviors that only exacerbate suffering. How many characters on t.v. fit this description?

It's all a question of perspective. The sun rising is a good thing, but in a land that is ravaged by drought, it can mean another day of devastation. Rain can be a good thing, too, but floods result when it doesn't cease falling. Human beings call things good or bad according to their circumstances. Good and bad things happen to the righteous and the unrighteous. Perspective is the key to one's response.

I left Cook County Hospital in 1955 for a position in the Department of Respiratory Care at Little Company of Mary Hospital in Evergreen Park, Illinois. I would serve there for thirty years. By now, I had a wife and two children to support. The Southwest side of Chicago was experiencing a population boom. Hospitals and health care services were expanding to an expanding need. It was a good time to be in medicine.

Little Company of Mary Hospital was a different culture from the one I had known at Cook County. While Cook County rested on humanistic values, Little Company of Mary reflected the Catholic principles of the congregation responsible for it.

The Little Company of Mary was founded in 1877 by Mother Mary Potter in Nottingham, England. Mother's hope was that her sisters would care for the suffering in the same spirit as Jesus' mother at the foot of the cross. As Mary looked upon her suffering son, so the Little Company of Mary sisters would look on all the suffering. The order's first five sisters cared for the sick and dying in a remodeled factory building.

In 1893, three LCM sisters arrived in the U.S. at the request of Charles Mair a prominent Chicago businessman whose wife had been cared for by the order in Rome. At first, the sisters occupied an eight-room cottage. For the next thirty-seven years, they visited the sick and dying of Chicago in their homes. The sisters soon found that there were many more people in need than they could handle. They lacked equipment, and travel in those days was difficult. Moreover, people in need of medical care had to travel miles to Mercy

Hospital in Chicago or St. Francis Hospital in Blue Island. The sisters needed a centrally located hospital building. With many prayers and little money, in the midst of a national economic depression, they acquired a tract of swampy land in Evergreen Park, Illinois. The four-story, 150-bed hospital they built was in the shape of a cross. Sitting prominently in a large niche in front, was a large statue of the Blessed Mother. At first, twelve physicians made up the entire staff. Residency options were only with the surgical or obstetrician departments. Care was available to everyone. An office visit cost as little as $10.00; it was free for those who could not pay.

Eventually, Little Company of Mary Hospital was able to add a nursing school, science building, convent, laboratory, cancer center, and emergency room. It became the preferred health care center for young couples beginning families. Since its opening, more than 200,000 babies have entered the world at Little Company of Mary, earning it the nickname "the Baby Hospital." The LCM sisters continued to expand their reach. By 1951, they had built Memorial Hospital and Health Care Center in Jasper, Indiana. A decade later they opened LCM Hospital in Torrance, California. Today, the LCMs can be found around the world serving as nurses, hospital administrators, parish ministers, spiritual directors, and social workers. They are an active voice for social justice.

Cook County Hospital and Little Company of Mary Hospital both exemplified the designation "place of hospitality." Yet, in a way, they represented two distinct cultures. One was a public hospital, and the other was a Catholic, not-for-profit hospital. The difference is evident in their mission statements. The 1986 Cook County Hospital mission statement read, "To provide a comprehensive program of quality health care, with respect and dignity, to the resident of Cook County, regardless of their ability to pay." The Little Company of Mary Foundation mission statement, however, identified the principles that guided it:

> In Solidarity with the Sisters of the Little Company of Mary, we are entrusted to serve the community through our ministry of Catholic Health Care. We are the empowered laity - the Greater Company of Mary. Rooted in a deep heritage of prayerful support of the sick and dying, we strive to enhance the sacredness of life and human dignity.[12]

As a nurse, my wife Eileen epitomized the spirituality of Little Company of Mary's mission. Her Catholic faith permeated all aspects of her life and work. She had grown up in the Beverly area on the Southside of Chicago, one of six children of Ray and Grace Carroll. She has said that, as a child, she thought everyone was Irish Catholic! Little Company of Mary Hospital was a big part of Eileen's life. She attended nursing school there, and then went on to deliver our eight children in its obstetrics ward.

During Eileen's senior year as a nursing student, medical history was made at Little Company of Mary Hospital. On June 17, 1950, a team of doctors led by Dr.

---

[12] Available at http://www.lcmh.org/index.cfm?pageID=303.

Richard Lawler performed the world's first intra-abdominal cadaveric renal transplant, in layman's terms, a kidney transplant. Two years earlier, at Loyola Medical School, Dr. Lawler, along with Doctors James West, Pat McNulty, Pat Murphy, and Edward Clancy, had experimented with kidney transplants on animals and cadavers. They were ready to try the procedure on a human being. The patient was Ruth Tucker, a 49 year-old woman whose mother and sister had already died of polycystic kidney disease and was herself in the final stages of the disease. Ruth's kidneys were shutting down. Dialysis was not yet available, and it was clear that she would die soon if something were not done. On that summer day in June, another 49 year-old woman with cirrhosis of the liver died in an adjacent operating room. A kidney was suddenly available. Dr. James West removed the kidney from the deceased donor and brought it to Dr. Lawler who then took an hour and a half replacing Tucker's left kidney. An intern, Dr. Zulo, along with Eileen's roommate, Mary Jane Maloney, assisted in the removal of the kidney from the donor. At least forty other doctors watched the surgery, with those in the back row standing on tables to get a better view. The surgery was a success, with the kidney functioning well for about fifty-three days, after which, it had to be removed due to the lack of immunity-suppressing drugs. In that time, however, Tucker's other kidney had recovered, and she lived another five years, succumbing eventually to heart failure, not kidney disease.

Dr. Lawler received both praise and condemnation for the transplant. He never did another one. He was quoted as saying that he just wanted to get such transplants started.

Lawler was truly an extraordinary man who put three brothers and himself through medical school. His hobby was photography, and he took over 30 pictures of the kidney transplant. His twin brothers, Doctors Paul and Frank Lawler, were renowned obstetricians who perfected the low-lying caesarian section. His other brother, Dr. Edmund Lawler, became a prominent pediatrician and author of the popular book *Birth to Birthday*. His assistant for the kidney transplant, Dr. James West, went on to become an expert in the treatment of alcoholism. He helped launch and then served as director of the Betty Ford Clinic.

Eileen wasn't the only one to witness groundbreaking medical advances. While I was at St. Francis Hospital in Blue Island, Illinois, the human heart was stopped and its functions taken over by an artificial pump that delivered oxygen to the vital tissues of the body. The cardiac surgeon used vein grafts to bypass the obstructive areas on the surface of the heart and replaced a diseased valve. This surgical procedure was introduced at research centers all over the United States by 1970, and in earnest at St. Francis Hospital in 1974.

An interesting question arose from these specialized treatments. Medical staff at St. Francis was equally divided as to the need for such procedures in a community hospital. Was it ethical to deprive patients of services for elective – and sometimes emergency surgeries – if too many beds were allotted to high priority, but not community-oriented procedures? The laws of the marketplace prevailed. The hospital was able to serve the interest of all our patients because administration and medical personnel rolled up their sleeves and worked in unison to pull it off.

Heated debates continued on both sides, however. Many specialists from surrounding clinics flooded our staff meetings. Money, of course, was always at issue. Just over two years earlier the hospital had completed a ten million dollar expansion, which netted the hospital a new eight-story, completely modern, 420-bed general surgical medical building across the street from its old facility. Could we justify more investment? Having served on the executive committee for several years, I was sympathetic to the opinions of both factions.

During this period, the southwest suburbs of Chicago underwent phenomenal population growth. Medical facilities were not adequate to the need. The city of Blue Island was over 100 years old; its hospital had been a landmark since 1905. The city fathers wanted to keep St. Francis Hospital in the city but were reluctant to donate their city park as a site for a new building. Many of the surrounding clinics, which provided the patient census, wished the hospital to move further southwest with the migrating center of the population. Fortunately, the decision to build in Blue Island in 1968 and to develop a cardiac center in 1974 proved wise in the end.

One woman in particular gets the credit for improved cardiac care in the area. Sister Helen Marie started asking for a pulmonary laboratory as far back as 1960. Her past experience as a respiratory therapist at St. Mary's Hospital in St. Louis, Missouri (the home of her motherhouse) had convinced her of the need for more advanced pulmonary care.

In 1974, I was happy to help Sister Helene Marie realize her dream. Our pulmonary laboratory began with one technician. By the time we moved into the new hospital in 1978, it boasted twenty employees.

The inception of cardiac surgery and new developments in pulmonary care, primarily respiratory and rapid blood gas analysis, eventually resulted in a respiratory care department of over forty people. Watching such great strides being made, I couldn't help but reminisce back to 1955 when we used Vanslykes machines and mercury manometers. At that time, it took about three hours to perform an arterial blood gas study. The machines we used in 1970 could do the same procedure, with accurate results, in less than five minutes.

Around this time, I set up a small private practice at 111th Street and Kedzie Avenue, but eventually joined forces with my brother, Eugene, a general surgeon, in a building we constructed at 113th and Western. What a difference this was from Cook County Hospital where patients lined the walls and occupied all the seats of the out-patient clinic! I often took my oldest son Bob with me in our Ford to make house calls and perform insurance examinations. I was qualified to practice the specialty of internal medicine at both Little Company of Mary and St. Francis Hospital, but preferred not to admit patients to those places if I could save them the cost of hospitalization.

I had one strict policy that I expected my male patients to observe: they had to bring their wives. My experience as a physician taught me that men were reluctant to admit feeling ill. It may have been pride, or the fact that being the primary breadwinner did not allow time for illness. In general, a wife was more vocal about her husband's symptoms than he was. Often, a wife saved her husband from a fatal coronary, a stroke, or possibly even death by cancer because of her concern over telltale signs and insistence that he go in for a check-up.

Once a week, I would drive out to Oak Forest Tuberculosis Hospital in Oak Forest, Illinois, as a consultant to children with tuberculosis. One by one the cottages were slowly closed down as antibiotic therapy eradicated the scourge. At the same time, the vast space between Evergreen Park and Oak Forest was slowly being "checker-boarded" in by housing developments. Chicago was experiencing major changes in the political and economic spheres, which in turn were responsible for its social makeover in the 60s and 70s. The transition from a "culture of life" to a "culture of death" had begun, particularly on the Southwest side of the city where "the good, the bad, and the ugly" were making history.

Chapter Five

---ᴧ/ᴧ⌒Ꙙᴧ/ᴧ---

Decade of Disillusionment

*Social action can assume various concrete
forms. It should always have the common good
in view and be in conformity with the message
of the Gospel and the teaching of the Church.
Catechism of the Catholic Church #2442*

I started this story with the observation that an
individual's story unfolds within the larger narrative of place,
family, and faith. My aim in these recollections is to illustrate
how our society moved from a culture of life to a culture of
death. In this and the following chapters, I am going to return
to the notion of place – to my home city of Chicago – as an
example of how new and twisted notions gradually laid claim
to our society. I will relate what I witnessed in my medical
practice and in the areas of life that directly concerned my
family, namely, the diocese of Chicago and its schools. In
some way, these memories could be those of any faithful
Catholic living through "the sixties" in America. During this
period, the subtle displacement of values I described in the last
chapter manifested itself. Evil worked its way out of the
woodwork and into the light of day. Nothing was sacred;

nothing remained untouched. Within a decade, the world was unrecognizable.

When I think of the sixties, the figure that looms largest for me is Chicago-born radical Saul Alinsky. His book *Rules for Radicals* was the bible for a movement of social activism that consciously targeted traditional values. Of his many progeny, our current president is the most famous. In 2009, Barak Obama won the Noble Prize for his work in "community organizing," a notion first promulgated by Alinsky. As a graduate student, his disciples educated Obama. He later received training from Alinsky's Industrial Areas Foundation and then spent several years teaching workshops on Alinksy's methods. His Noble Prize was the result of a four-year stint working for the Developing Communities Project, an Alinsky organization. Obama went on to work with ACORN and Project Vote – also Alinsky-inspired groups. If you want to understand our president's perspective on social change, all you need do is consider Saul Alinsky.

On the surface, he looked like a do-gooder out to improve the living conditions of the poor in North America. His special focus was the African-American ghettoes of the country's major cities. Alinsky's radical methods appealed to counterculture, college students who applied them in campus protests. He was as blatant about his goals as Margaret Sanger had been about her desire to eliminate "inferior" races. One has only to read the dedication page of Alinsky's book to understand the nature of his ideology:

Lest we forget at least an over the shoulder acknowledgment to the very first radical: from all our legends, mythology and history (and who is to know where mythology leaves off and history begins - or which is which), the very first radical known to man who rebelled against the establishment and did it so effectively that he at least won his own kingdom - Lucifer.[13]

Inspired by the Prince of Darkness, Alinsky drew his philosophical principles from the writings of Marx and Lenin. His end game was nothing other than the realization of the communist agenda. In 1972, he admitted his ties to communism in an interview with *Playboy Magazine*:

> I knew plenty of Communists in those days, and I worked with them on a number of projects. Back in the Thirties, the Communists did a hell of a lot of good work; they were in the vanguard of the labor movement and they played an important role in aiding blacks and Okies and Southern sharecroppers. Anybody who tells you he was active in progressive causes in those days and never worked with the Reds is a goddamn liar. Their platform stood for all the right things, and unlike many liberals, they were willing to put their bodies on the line . . . I was in charge of a big part of fund raising for the International

---

[13] Saul D. Alinsky, *Rules for Radicals: A Pragmatic Primer for Realistic Radicals* (New York, NY: Vintage Books, 1972).

Brigade and in that capacity I worked in close
alliance with the Communist Party.[14]

So much for Saul Alinksy. What is particularly saddening is
that the Catholic Church in Chicago bought in to Alinsky's
program. They joined with him and his people to crush the
culture of the Chicago stock yards, a culture that was based on
old world faith and values. A little history may be helpful at
this point. The invention of the refrigerated boxcar led to an
expansion of meatpacking plants in an area of New City
known as the "Back of the Yards." This area employed
thousands of European immigrants in the early 20th century.
Back of the Yards was settled first by Irish and German
butchers, and later by Czechs, Poles, Lithuanians, and
Slovaks. You can read a description of life in the stockyards
in Upton Sinclair's novel *The Jungle* (1906).

By the1950s, this was the largest livestock yard and
meatpacking center in the nation. But it was more than that. It
was a unique place where the values of the old world were
strong. The ethnic communities organized themselves around
Catholic parishes; priests and sisters were brought over from
the homeland. These parishes preserved the faith and culture
of the people. They also provided a social framework in the
form of men and women's clubs and sports associations.
Unfortunately, when the meatpacking industry of Chicago
faded out in the 1960s, Back of the Yards experienced
economic depression and structural disintegration.

---

[14] *Playboy*, March 1972. Available at
https://thealinsky.wordpress.com/2013/04/11/saul-alinsky-interview-part-
10/.

Up until the Depression, the residents of Back of the Yards handled their problems themselves. Eventually, two social movements emerged: the Packinghouse Workers Organizing Committee (UPWA-CIO) and the Back of the Yards Neighborhood Council (BYNC). The UPWA-CIO worked to raise wages and improve work conditions. The BYNC reached further, aligning itself with ethnic groups and addressing social justice concerns. Alinsky stepped in and used these movements to hone a model for social change that he would later apply elsewhere in the United States.

It's amazing how evil can so easily creep in the back door. The name "Lucifer" comes from the Latin word for "light." True to his name, the Prince of Lies appears to bring light when, in fact, he is peddling a distortion of the truth. Alinksy and other communist radicals of the time wore the mantle of light. Their rhetoric and their activism looked as though it were in service to the poor and marginalized. The men of the Church, deceived by appearances, formed a partnership with them. Little by little, the false ideals informing these efforts lodged themselves in the minds of those working in the name of the Gospel.

Jesus told his disciples, "The poor you will always have with you." One of the false promises of a social activism not inspired by faith is the prospect of eliminating poverty. In the name of correcting this and every other wrong, social reformers replaced long-standing social structures – like the Back of the Yards – with new structures that failed to respect basic human rights. While it's true that the Back of the Yards was no paradise, Alinsky and his cohorts had no right to throw the baby out with the bathwater. An entire culture fell under the axe of a new, secular order.

Knowing this history sheds some light on the last eight years of the present administration in Washington. Did any of us fully realize what Barack Obama meant when he promised us "change"? A quick look at his mentors and activism tells us that the change he sought meant the end of Christian institutions. Since his election, he has made this program absolutely clear. Hobby Lobby and the Hawthorne Sisters of New York have been hard-pressed to fight the implications of Obamacare.

I have known another kind of politics and another kind of politician. Despite the limitations that originate in original sin, human beings can govern wisely and well. Faith and ethnic identity is no obstacle to good governance. I will give you an example.

For 150 years, the Irish pretty much ruled Chicago. The southwest side of the city was the work of Mayor Richard Joseph Daley. Like me, he was a graduate of De La Salle High School. He worked as a stockyards cowboy while attending law school. In the late 1940s and early 1950s, Daley was busy raising a family of seven children. In 1955, as Mayor of Chicago, he attended Mass daily and was a father figure regarded by most as an honest man. He took the slogan "Good government is good politics." His legacy as mayor included building projects, youth centers, transit systems, public works, and recreational areas. What most people remember him for today is the family-friendly St. Patrick's Day Parade on

Western Ave. I remember him for much more. He was an example of faith in practice.

In the time I'm describing, faith and identity imparted the spiritual values that informed decision-making. Sadly, as our city grew in material wealth, it also declined in spiritual values. The loss of these values meant the loss of a culture. In *The Religious Crisis of the 1960s*, historian Hugh McLeod describes what he calls "the decline of Christendom." He defines Christendom as a society in which there are close links between the elites of church and society, where laws are said to be based on Christian principles, and where the majority of people are presumed to be Christian.[15] By the early 1960s, Christendom in this sense was crumbling. Governing bodies grew more separate from the churches. The expression "separation of church and state" became the mantra of a secular order in which the government strove to create a perfect world – the "Great Society," as Lyndon Johnson put it. Law making ceased to be the mechanism of social harmony, the means by which people could live together in peace and pursue life, liberty, and happiness. Laws became the tools of social engineering. Judges looked not to the original intentions of the country's founders, but to the goals of contemporary civil rights movements. As for assuming most people were Christian, the very notion of what it meant to be Christian changed. Although church attendance stayed strong

---

[15] Hugh McLeod, *The Religious Crisis of the 1960s* (New York: NY, Oxford University Press, 2007).

throughout the sixties, for the most part ambition for wealth and luxury replaced the hope of salvation.

The collapse of Christendom did not take long to manifest in the nation's youth. Many young adults had begun to question the beliefs of their parents. They felt that their parents' values were not enough to help them deal with the social and racial difficulties of the time. Young people are by nature honest and passionate for what they believe. The hypocrisy of their elders and the lack of any grounding in traditional faith and morals created a moral and spiritual void that was quickly filled by "sex, drugs, and rock n' roll." A new culture of youth sprang into being, one that challenged authority at home and in the universities.

Women's interests changed radically, too. The feminists who emerged in the sixties were not the suffragettes who had won the right to vote for women. The women's movement ceased promoting the uniqueness and dignity of women as women and took for its goal the transformation of women into men. The manifestation of this shift was the push for a so-called "Equal Rights Amendment." The ERA meant enshrining in the law of the land the complete leveling sexual distinctions between men and women. By the time the ERA was on the agenda, the mechanisms for this leveling were in place. The Pill promised women the same sexual freedom as men. States began changing their abortion laws, too. When the Pill failed, there would be abortion available. Women were no longer to be "burdened" by pregnancy. The economy, too, helped to unsex women. Two-income families became the norm. Day-care came into being. Young women were told that family was a secondary priority; what they needed to think about first was career and self-realization. By 1966, women were one-third of the labor force, with a median age over forty. The fastest growing segment was mothers of young children. The traditional idea that "women's place is in the home" was clearly out of date. The first objective of the new movement was to declare "woman's place is in the world."[16]

My wife and I married and started our family in a world that little by little was slipping into the past. In past times, laypeople could count on the Church to provide guidance and ensure the teachings that define Christian life and belief. Those times were no longer. By Divine Providence, we were armed for the battle ahead by a special experience of divine grace.

In 1966, Eileen and I traveled to Rome. The Holy See had just recognized the International Federation of Catholic Medical Associations as an International Catholic Organization. As members, we gathered with delegates from sixty-six other countries for the 11th Medical Services Week. After many visits to the historical treasures of Rome, we attended the general audience with Pope Paul VI at Castle Gondolfo. Present were Bishop Fulton Sheen, Count Mario Stoppa, Bishop Marcinkas, and the superior general of the Christian Brothers. This was truly an international gathering. The Holy Father spoke to each group in their native tongue and ended with the Apostles Creed in Latin.

---

[16] Leila J. Rupp and Verta Taylor, *American Women's Rights Movement, 1945 to the 1960s* (New York: NY, Oxford University Press, 1987).

The next day was the climax of our trip: a private audience with the Vicar of Christ. Pat Daley Thompson, daughter of Mayor Richard Daley, had arranged it for us. Pat and her new husband were on their honeymoon, and we were pleased that they allowed us to share this momentous occasion with them. We drove past St. Peter's Basilica and were admitted to Vatican City where we were met by members of the Swiss Guard. Upon presentation of our credentials, we were escorted to the second floor of the Papal Palace in the Vatican. Here we were greeted by Count Mario Stoppa of the Vatican staff and escorted to the room where we would meet the pope. He arrived accompanied by several aids. After taking his seat upon a raised dais, the Holy Father greeted each us. He gave me a medal, a remembrance of his papacy, and I wished him a reign of many years. Eileen and I returned home, tired but renewed in spirit. Little did we know what challenges lay ahead for us.

At this time, I was busy starting a private practice. It was hard to balance life and family, and time was in short supply. Nonetheless, Eileen and I realized we could not stand at the sidelines while our deepest beliefs were being challenged from every side. We made the decision to be more involved in the parish life of our church. We also made a move to defend traditional family values by joining the Christian Family Movement.

Pat and Patty Crowley had been way ahead of the curve in regards to societal change and the family. In 1945, with the support of Cardinal Stritch of Chicago, they founded the Christian Family Movement with the goal of reinforcing

Christian values and providing encouragement to parents as they fulfilled their divinely-given mission. Small groups of five to seven families met in one another's home or in parish centers. These were no mere social gatherings. At their meetings, CFM members shared what they were observing in their family lives, their neighborhoods, and what was happening in the wider culture. Members practiced the method of "observe-judge-act." Out of these meetings came involvement in foster care, refugee sponsorship, prison ministry, couple counseling, and religious education. The wives of CFM members formed a group that evolved into the Pre-Cana Conference, the Catholic Church's form of marriage preparation. The CFM received the official recognition of the Church. By 1966, it had groups in more than 50 nations. CFM was one of the first Catholic lay-apostolate movements, well ahead of the call to the laity in Vatican Council II.

For a while, Eileen and I were enthusiastic members of CFM. At a certain point, however, we noticed that meeting discussions were focusing more and more on "bringing the American Church into the modern world." At the center of these speculations was the question of contraception. No other topic has so ripped apart the Church today as contraception. The history of the CFM is a case in point.

In 1964, the Crowleys were invited by Pope Paul VI to take part in the Papal Birth Control Commission to advise the pope on the morality of new contraceptive methods. The Crowleys were one of three married couples chosen for the group whose role was not authoritative, but informative. Earlier meetings had been composed entirely of clergy, medical doctors, psychologists, and social scientists. The Crowleys presented the results of a survey of married couples that revealed how painful (and unsuccessful) most Catholic couples found the practice of rhythm, the church's sole approved method of birth control. The commission eventually published a report advocating the reversal of the Church's ban on birth control. Two years later, however, Paul VI issued the encyclical *Humanae Vitae* flatly rejecting the commission's proposal. The encyclical declared that the prohibition of contraception would remain in force. It also re-affirmed the Church's teaching on the dignity of marriage and the moral problems inherent in artificial birth control.

Years later, following the death of Patty Crowley, The National Catholic Reporter, renowned for its liberal editorial stance on numerous doctrinal and moral issues, recounted the Crowleys' participation in the commission and their lives afterwards. The article revealed that "the decision, as dismissive of the work of many experts, came as an especially hard blow to the Crowleys. Patty and Pat were quite open and public in expressing their disappointment."[17]

What was even more alarming then dissent from Catholic lay movements was the opposition of the clergy. The Washington Post and the Chicago Sun Times both carried front-page photos of Catholic protesters of *Humanae Vitae*, all of whom were wearing Roman collars. Most Catholics had never seen anything like this before. The idea that priests were doing the protesting was shocking, and it led many Catholics

[17]http://www.natcath.org/NCR_Online/achives2/2005d/120905/120905o.php.

to wonder how bishops and theologians could disagree on such an important subject. This resulted in a weakening of the authority of the Church to teach on other topics.

By 1968, Eileen and I were one of over 10,000 couples who had broken away from the Christian Family Movement. We got involved with Pre-Cana instruction. I was approached by the head of the physician's speakers to offer some of my free time to this important project. I gave him my phone number. Every so often, we crossed each other's paths in the corridors, and he would broach the subject of my speaking to couples on the Catholic Church's teaching on marriage. Eileen and I worked hard preparing materials for the marriage talks, but never received the call.

One day, while making my rounds at Little Company of Mary Hospital, I ran into my colleague Dr. J. Kampner, an obstetrician and gynecologist. Dr. Kampner also taught Pre-Cana courses. He confided in me his difficulty presenting marriage courses to engaged couples. His talks reflected what the Catholic Church had always taught, that is, that marriage is a covenant, a source of grace for each of the spouses. This message was seldom well received any more. Even in our own ranks, *Humanae Vitae* had received little support. Despite the pope's pastoral directives to "men of science" and to doctors, urging them to look for natural ways of regulating birth, the Physician Speakers Guild did not call on Dr. Kampner or me to discuss marriage from a Christian physician's viewpoint.

Dr. Herbert Ratner, editor of the magazine *Child and Family*, described how the Pre-Cana movement slid from a small error in the beginning to a fatal vision at the end. At the heart of the problem was "the disassociation of conjugal love from the sense in which procreation and education of children was central (and essential) to the natural institute of marriage . . . What resulted was inevitable. The engaged couples picked up the error [since it] seemed to have the Church's stamp of approval of secular attitudes and values."

Moral issues abounded during the sixties. The radical and accelerated pace of social change surrounded us. By 1968, the Civil Rights Movement had already been going strong for ten years. Protests against the war in Vietnam, which started between pacifist and leftists in campus "teach-ins" were gaining strength. They began in earnest after the United States military started regular bombings against North Vietnam.

At home, Eileen and I made it a point to educate our children on American law. We often read the Constitution to them. They understood that the right to freedom of expression and peaceful protest is crucial in a democracy. The exchange of information and ideas is essential to public accountability and transparency in government. My son Bob grasped clearly that the law of our land resides in the judicial system. Interpretation of the law by the courts is sometimes just and sometimes wide of the mark. The Dred Scott Case of 1857 found the Supreme Court declaring that "negroes" had "no rights which any white man was bound to respect."[18] Of course, the Supreme Court's worst miscarriage of justice was their 1973 decision in Roe v. Wade. It is interesting that the courts in this country allowed DNA testing in many of their

---

[18] This quote is from the opinion of Chief Justice Robert B. Taney.
Although each justice wrote his own opinion, Taney's is the most known.

deliberations, recognizing that DNA is the genetic blueprint of a unique human being, yet did nothing to promote the unique identity of a human embryo. The courts today have, in effect, declared that some people have rights and some can be killed with impunity. Is it any wonder that our children are shooting each other in our public schools? Thanks to our judicial system, life is cheap in the United States.

In the midst of a world in crisis, ordinary life continued. In the summer of 1968, Eileen and I piled everyone in the car for a week of vacation in Michigan. Ten people, a dog, and a load of suitcases squeezed into a station wagon with a roof carrier were a fairly common site on Interstate 94 every summer. We started our trip, as we did all our trips, with a prayer, and we were off. The hot sun and arid air caused us to stop for drinks – and then bathrooms – once or twice during the trip. At one stop, our son Jackie, endowed with a marked vision defect, was forced to run after our station wagon after it had slowly pulled away without him. Apparently, while in the store, he was engrossed in a comic book when we reboarded. We neglected to count noses. A driver pulled up to let us know a small lad was chasing us. "Did we really think we could sneak away?" The driver laughed as he pointed back a half block. After Jackie climbed into the car, I recalled how a friend of ours had left one child out of their family of nine in a downtown restaurant late in the evening and didn't discover his absence until they arrived home in the suburbs. The police were waiting at the door with the news. So it could have been worse!

It was about dusk when we arrived at the resort. Everyone cleared out from the back window and both doors before we had come to a complete stop. Recognizing their friends from previous years on the baseball diamond, shuffleboard, and Ping-Pong tables, the kids couldn't wait to join in. Mrs. Lang, the proprietor of the resort, welcomed us at the office looking perplexed. We had come the wrong week. We were not due until the following Saturday. And, of course, reservations for ten people were unheard of. We huddled back into the station wagon (this time using the buddy system!) and started the discouraged trek back home to Chicago. The following week we returned to the Michigan resort, and perhaps for the better. The Chicago Democratic Convention was in all its glory on national television, and we were thankful to be viewing it from a distance.

Historically, the convention stands as a pivotal event. In the fall of 1967, the Democratic Party decided to hold its 1968 national convention and the expected re-nomination of President Lyndon Johnson in Chicago. Mayor Richard Daley promised his city would be free of civil disorders. Yet, by the summer of 1968, the prospect of a smooth convention had vanished. Johnson, in the face of growing protests against the Vietnam War, withdrew from the presidential race in March. Martin Luther King, Jr., was assassinated in April, provoking urban riots in Chicago and other cities. The assassination of Robert Kennedy in June further shocked the nation and complicated the race for the Democratic nomination.

Young peace activists and anti-Vietnam protesters were forming and contributing to the social unrest. Many

Democrats wished to move the convention, but Mayor Daley would not let the convention leave Chicago. He promised to enforce the peace and not allow outrageous demonstrations.

Fortunately, the cottages at our Michigan resort did not have television sets, so the large group of parents would gather in the dining hall for a recap of the day's convention highlights. The children at the resort, probably sixty to seventy of them, were always so exhausted from the day's activities that they were already asleep. It was hard to watch what was happening in Chicago. The worst day of protesting was dubbed "the battle of Michigan Avenue." Protestors were stopped in their march to the convention site and the media recorded graphic violence against them on the part of the Chicago police. Many hotels where the delegates were staying were affected by the riots. Fumes from the tear gas used by the police and "stink bombs" thrown by the protesters drifted into the buildings. Total disobedience to legitimate authority as the theme was what the television media attempted to portray. Many Chicago policemen and elected officials were patients of mine.

Later, I viewed the media's film and certain frames were missing. One in particular was very interesting. A bearded radical with a baseball bat struck Danny Creedon, a Chicago police sergeant, with a blow to his shoulder. He instinctively responded, waving his nightstick for protection from another blow. The radical ducked just as another picture was taken. When this photo was sent through AP international, it was front-page news worldwide: a "bully policeman" wielding his nightstick over a defenseless radical.

Nothing could have been further from the truth. A second clip showed three helmeted Chicago policemen attacking a group of radicals, but in a defensive pose. This same picture was in *Life* magazine nine months later with a caption description of a scene in New York! Accuracy was seriously lacking in media reporting. Deceptive language and images began to permeate the news.

In light of events at the 1968 Democratic Convention in Chicago, I was convinced that changes in the political, social, and religious climate were taking place in our nation. Sides were being taken, and the line was drawn in the sand. We were once a society based on personal responsibility. This was the primary ethic we strove to teach our children. Slowly, that focus shifted toward teaching social responsibility. Society, not the individual, was responsible. As a result, the absolute wrongs of murder, lying, and stealing became less absolute. The criterion for just punishment was disregarded. New stories on violent crimes or tragedies became more focused on the perpetrator. It seemed to soothe or calm them to find a reason for a violent action. Some went to great lengths to find the grey area that justified criminal actions.

My son Jack and I had a small experience of this new ethical standard when he was a freshman at the local seminary high school. He told me that someone had taken a ten dollar bill that he had left on his locker shelf while in gym. I called the priest in charge of the school expecting him to be aware of a possible thief in the student ranks, but he prefaced his unconcern by declaring that the one who took the money probably needed it more than my son did. This was illogical thinking. Wrong is wrong, and causation is irrelevant. That this sentiment came from the head of a supposedly well-financed, large faculty body of a superbly built high school meant disaster for the moral fiber of the institution. Graffiti was already inside lockers and in the bathrooms. Decline continued unabated, and within ten years, student enrollment had fallen considerably.

The great social planners of the time promoted causes for the right reasons. Gun control advocates came out in full force by 1968 after the killings of Martin Luther King, Jr., and Robert Kennedy, not to mention several summers of race-related riots occurring in American cities. While the Black Panthers were protesting the new gun control laws, the nation's politicians and 60% of Americans feared that violence was too prevalent and too many people had access to guns. I had firsthand experience of gun availability.

While I was director of the Department of Respiratory Care at St. Francis Hospital, Dr. Norman Schwartz and I exchanged polarized opinions about gun control. I carried a gun as a Navy officer on watch duty in the Pacific, but did not own a gun as a civilian. Nevertheless, I felt that possession of a gun was protected by the Constitution, and the intent to license guns was just money in their pockets. Dr. Schwartz adamantly supported gun control. He felt there were too many deaths by guns and to stop the carnage, gun control was necessary.

Two years later, in May of 1970, I was sitting in my department office when I heard a loud exchange of voices down the hall. As I opened the door, shots rang out. I assumed they were directed at me and ran back into my office for cover. Not finding any sign of injury on myself, I returned to the door. Two nurses from the emergency room further down the hall followed into the room. As I opened the door, I confronted Dr. Norman Schwartz with a gun in his hand, wrapped in a towel. Behind him, I could see Dr. Fuentes lying on his back with a fatal gunshot wound to the heart. Dr. Schwartz later claimed that the shooting was in self-defense. The words from Dr. Bartlett summed up what some of us felt at the time: "If guns are licensed and controlled, only the criminal would possess them." How right he was! Dr. Schwartz's story was just one example of a movement away from individual responsibility.

President Ronald Reagan had this to say about personal responsibility: "We must reject the idea that every time a law is broken, society is guilty rather than the lawbreaker. It is time to restore the American precept that each individual is accountable for his actions."[19]

The change in traditional beliefs within the secular culture of the sixties was paralleled by changes in the faith and practice of Christian churches. The Catholic Church's Second Vatican Council, as it was called, reaffirmed much of traditional teaching, but the ambiguity of its language often left the door open to novel interpretations. After its closing in 1965, the "Spirit of the Council" became a catch phrase justifying a multitude of changes in every aspect and at every level of Catholic life and worship. This had not been the

---

[19] Speech at the Republican National Convention, Platform Committee Meeting, Miami, Florida (31 July 1968).

original intent of the council. John XXIII had opened the Council, declaring, "The principle aim of the Vatican Council is this: that the sacred deposit of Christian doctrine be more effectively guarded and taught."[20] The word used was "guarded," not "changed." Unfortunately, people within the church summarily and without any authority – and certainly without reading the Vatican Council's published documents – rearranged and recast traditional ways of thinking, praying, and worshipping. The Mass became a pale reflection of its former glory, using the vernacular language and popular musical styles. Churches were stripped of altar rails and traditional images, the latter being replaced by new artistic forms difficult for the faithful to interpret. Many Catholics understood that the Council had called for a conversion of life, fidelity to the Gospel and all of those things that had always been part of Christian belief and practice. However, there were others who seized the opportunity to advance personal agendas, justifying their efforts in the name of the Council. Some radical notions may have been due to ignorance and an overzealous desire to make the Church "relevant." Some, however, were clear sighted and deliberate.

It is difficult to think of any area of Catholic life that was not somehow impacted by the misinterpretations of Vatican Council II. One thing that was particularly evident was the lack of respect for authority at all levels of the Church. There were conflicts in Catholic schools, colleges, and universities. They occurred in parishes, even on the altar itself,

---

[20] Available at http://www.ourladyswarriors.org/teach/v2open.htm.

in the name of liturgical experimentation. A misguided reform of the liturgy followed the Council; it unfolded in disobedience, guided only by the sentiments of the reformers. Ecumenism leveled the differences between the various religions. Compromises to the true faith were justified by the need to reclaim Christian unity. A spirit of disobedience prevailed and led to the loss among priests and religious of the true sense of their vocations. Seminaries taught the tenets of Modernism in various forms and attacked the perennial position of the Church, re-affirmed by Pope Paul VI, prohibiting birth control. A "vocation crisis" emerged as fewer and fewer young people offered their lives to Christ in service of the Church as priests and religious. Cardinal Ratzinger, later Pope Benedict XVI, expressed his view of what happened:

> I am convinced the damage that we have incurred in these years is due, not to the true Council, but to the unleashing within the Church of latent polemical and centrifugal forces; and outside the Church, it is due to the confrontation with a cultural revolution in the West: the success of the upper middle class, the new "tertiary bourgeoisie," with is liberal-radical ideology of individualistic, rationalistic, and hedonistic stamp.[21]

The rift in the Church was particularly hard on religious sisters and nuns who for generations had been the face of Catholicism

---

[21] *The Ratzinger Report* (San Francisco, CA: Ignatius Press, 1985), 27-33

in America by their service in hospitals and schools. They had been the pioneers of health care, education, and social work in the United States. It was a normal occurrence to see them in their distinctive religious habits. As time went by, many orders set aside their habits in favor of clothing similar to those worn by the people they served. Some communities, however, went too far. The document *Perfectae Caritatis* clarified the importance of the religious habit:

> The religious habit, an outward mark of consecration to God, should be simple and modest, poor and at the same time becoming. In addition, it must meet the requirements of health and be suited to the circumstances of time and place and to the needs of the ministry involved. The habits of both men and women religious which do not form to these norms *must be changed.*[22]

The key word here is "changed." The document does not say "eliminated." Yet, how many orders today have no visible sign of consecration, no habit that distinguishes them in terms expressed in this directive?

As a result of the so-called "renewal" of religious life, long-standing communities lost members, and few young women stepped up to take their place. The lack of vocations precipitated a radical decline in Catholic institutions. Once

---

[22] *Perfectae Caritatis*, Vatican II Decree on the Adaptation of Renewal of Religious Life.

"do your own thing" replaced "follow Christ," there was little to attract young people to the convents and seminaries.

Within three years after the close of Vatican Council II, an unusually large number of priests and sisters started showing up in my office with physical complaints. Many of them suffered from peptic ulcers, elevated blood pressure, and other diseases caused by stress. At first, I was unaware of the common causes of such symptoms, but after much discussion with sisters suffering these things, I concluded that the stress they endured was the result of ridicule directed at them by younger members of their communities. The sisters were shamed for wearing their religious habits. The priests were criticized for saying private prayers and devotions and for adhering to Catholic principles concerning papal authority, confession, daily Mass, and the avoidance of unnecessary social contacts.

One day, an emotionally distraught, elderly sister came into my office. My brother had removed her spleen ten years previously at my request because of a severe, chronic, and disabling blood condition. I thought she had been cured and marveled at how active she was as a high school teacher. Was it possible she had relapsed? An examination determined sister was in good health. After a few minutes' conversation, however, it appeared she was being forced back into the world. I learned that she had not been to a shopping center for thirty years. She preferred wearing the shoes and habit of her order. Now, her younger superiors were telling her that she must remove her habit, visit a shoe store for stylish shoes, and have her hair done. Mentally, sister could not cope with these drastic changes. She was not alone.

The young sisters now in authority were unrelenting in their purging. Some sisters asked for dispensations of their vows and left to teach in secular schools. Roles were reversed, curriculums changed, and social study textbooks from secular schools replaced Church history texts. Dissenters flooded Catholic colleges and high schools, determined to uproot traditional thinking and practice. Catholic hospitals soon followed.

In 1994, The Los Angeles Times conducted a survey of 1049 nuns in the United States and Puerto Rico. Only three percent were forty years of age or younger; thirty-seven percent were older than seventy; and twelve percent were over the age of eighty. The Times discovered that the median age for Catholic nuns was – at the time – sixty-five years old. "American Catholics have no idea how very soon there will be no nuns," Sister Patricia Wittberg, a church sociologist, told the Los Angeles Times, while Sister Eleane King, a research associate, added, "It tells me that the majority of religious congregations of women in this country will not survive. More are dying."[23] Truly, we have seen the end of an era for the Catholic Church in America.

We have covered a lot of ground in this chapter. My purpose has been to illustrate the breakdown of traditional values in many areas, inside and outside of the Catholic

---

[23] Stammer, Larry B. (1994, February 21). Number of Nuns on Brink of Precipitous Drop. *The LA Times*. Retrieved from http://www.latimes.com.

Church. In each case, the optimistic ideal of "change" did not produce its promised fruit. On the contrary, enormous personal suffering and social upheaval followed. As a physician, I saw firsthand the devastating effects of a new, secular culture on my patients and their families. Our Savior gave us a way of evaluating human activity: "By their fruits you will know them." I believe it is time to speak frankly about the fruits of the "progressive" ideals that have been shaping life and policy in this country for the last fifty years. In the simplest possible terms: they don't work.

Bob in 3rd grade at St. Dorothy School. Third row, second from the right.

Football for De La Salle High School

1944. Robert as a Naval Officer stationed on Kwajalein Island. Manager of WXLG Armed Forces Radio Network.

1945 Graduation from St. Mary's College

Bob and his mother, 1945

Bob with his brother, Eugene

Bob with his brother, Fr. John

Nurse, Eileen (nee Carroll) Dolehide, at both Little Company of Mary Hospital and University of Chicago.

Our Wedding, October 11, 1952

Bob and Eileen with 7 of their 8 children.

Bottom left: Michelle, Maureen Top: Bobby holding Mary, Brian holding Kathy, and Jackie holding Kevin (Kathy's twin).

Fr. John, Eugene, Noreen and Robert Dolehide

Eileen and Dr. & Mrs. Diamond at the Abstinence Council on the Family

Robert Dolehide protesting at Chicago's Daly Center after the Roe vs. Wade Supreme Court

Chicago Tribune article of Eileen Dolehide with Phylis Schafly, founder of Eagle Forum.

Dr. Robert Dolehide was awarded the Presidential Award for Outstanding Merit from Saint Mary's University of Minnesota May 17, 2014.

Dr. Dolehide with son, Kevin, who worked alongside his father at the Chicago's 113th and Western location.

On May 19, 2014, after 55 years in the same building, Dr. Dolehide was joined by his family and honored with an official street sign designation: Dr. Dolehide Way.

Kevin & Brian Dolehide with Cardinal Burke

Our 40th Wedding Anniversary

Robert & Eileen, as of this printing, have been blessed with 46 grandchildren and 8 great-grandchildren.

Sons, Brian & Kevin with the Order of Malta

Grandson, Steven Stoll with daughter, Mary

2004, Robert & Eileen greeting
the now St. John Paul II

Servant of God, Fr.
John Hardon, and Saint
Theresa of Calcutta
were who Dr. Dolehide
found his motivating
energy. In the words of
Mother Teresa: "We
must be sincere and
treat people one on
one."

Chapter Six

Culture Battles

*Choose you this day whom you will serve . . . As
for me and my house, we will serve the Lord –
Joshua 24:15*

One hears a lot today from feminists about the terrible
old days when women stayed at home and men went to work.
The gist of the message is that men had all the fun, while
women were isolated and imprisoned. Looking back to the
very time in question, I have to say that the truth has been
almost entirely obscured. There was no plot to keep men
happy and women miserable. There was the reality of raising
a family together and the need for someone to make a living
and someone to make a home.

My wife and I enjoyed equal responsibility for the
raising of our family notwithstanding the different ways in
which we realized that end. There was never any doubt in our
minds that my work at the office and Eileen's work in the
home were anything other than a distribution of tasks
necessary for our common effort. Truth be told, of the two of
us, I see Eileen's task as the one deserving more praise since
it fell to her to integrate our shared values and aims within the

context of a loving and well-ordered home life. This she did with extraordinary grace and intelligence.

By 1976, my practice was growing rapidly, but so were the number of mouths we had to feed at home. I did not see my time at work as an escape from the home front. In fact, I often felt the tension of having, on the one hand, the responsibilities of a husband and father, and on the other, the need to give my full attention to my patients. As my practice expanded, I had less and less time to spend at home. When a man chooses the life of physician, he chooses to be a public servant. He cannot always give to his family what he would like. He has a duty to be available to his patients. On those occasions when I acted curtly to someone at the office or the hospital, I regretted it later. The sick do not wish themselves sick. When they approach a physician, they have the right to find medical expertise and a full attentive, listening ear. Sometimes, that latter is worth more than all the medicines in the world. But, on occasion, the effort to manage my professional and personal life was a strain, and I did give in to impatience.

My wife was always my salvation. Inadvertently, she would hear me on the phone in conversations with or about patients. She would catch me expressing my frustration. Afterward, she would remind me that the person on the other end of the line was just as important as the President of the United States and should be treated as such. I was always amazed at her selflessness. How many wives are so generous with their husbands? How many are willing to play second fiddle to those who are in need? In truth, my wife and I constituted a team, not only in regards to raising our children, but also in what concerned my medical practice.

I needed all the patience I could get to deal with rapid changes in the way we doctors could practice medicine. I will give you an example of how independent practice and initiative grew more and more threatened by "orders from above."

There is a dictum in medicine: Never be the first nor the last to use a particular type of therapy. In 1959, the FDA approved the marketing of Triparanol as a cholesterol-lowering agent. Many of my patients asked for it. I assured them that, if after two years, the medical reports concluded its safety, I would prescribe it. For some of my patients, my caution was not sufficient. They insisted on receiving the medication. I held to my stance. Just before I was finally ready to give in to their demands, medical journals started filling up with articles connecting cataracts to the medication. In 1962, it was withdrawn from the market after the FDA discovered that the manufacturer had provided falsified laboratory data that omitted reference to the cataracts found in rats and dogs in pre-clinical trials. Some patients who had taken the drug for a year also developed cataracts.[24]

A significant part of this story is the independence I enjoyed as a private health care provider. I had the right (and responsibility) to decline to prescribe Triparanol because I believed it lacked the test of time. Since those days,

---

[24] Laughlin, RC and Carey, TF, "Cataracts in Patients with Triparanol." *JAMA* 181: July 1962, 339-40.

government has sought to overcome resistance to new forms of medical intervention by denying health care providers a say in the treatment they prescribe.

Fifteen years after the Triparanol catastrophe, the Swine Flu epidemic gave the government the opening it needed. President Gerald Ford issued a warning about a possible outbreak of the virus following the death of an army recruit and the illness of several other soldiers. It was a case of hype leading to catastrophe. In response to his warning, a nationwide vaccination program was initiated. The Chicago newspapers picked up on this grandiose, "humanitarian" enterprise that Washington had decided was good for us. Before the facts were properly examined, the Swine Flu vaccine was distributed throughout the United States at great cost to the taxpayer. The local health board required that I make the vaccination available to every patient who requested it.

As a senior member of my private clinic, I stood firm against this intrusion. I was not alone. The newspaper and electronic media chastised those of us in private practice for not falling to our knees in obedience to federal law. How could we turn away an elderly, poor person because he could not pay for the Swine Flu vaccine? They assumed that because the federal government had directed us to distribute the vaccine for free our reason for not doing so was economic. Any and all professional concerns were swept under the carpet, making those of us who protested the vaccine look greedy and self-serving.

In fact, I had carefully studied the epidemiological reasons for the vaccine's use, how it was obtained, and how it was to be distributed. Consequently, I knew that the vaccine was potentially dangerous. The experimental data was sadly lacking. I informed the office staff of my reservations and told them that patients seeking vaccination for Swine Flu should be directed to the local city health clinic.

It wasn't long before patients started showing up at the hospitals and private clinics such as my own with strange symptoms that could not be explained. The only common denominator was that they had all received the Swine Flu vaccine. More than 40 million Americans received the Swine Flu immunization. In the weeks that followed, evidence emerged that the vaccine increased the risk for Guillain-Barre syndrome, a nerve disease. I saw as much and more in my own practice. One man developed a nephrotic syndrome that I had not seen in years. His kidney tubulars were blocked by an infectious/toxic substance, causing him to swell from the tip of his head to his toes. He lost a tremendous amount of albumin through his kidneys. He was hospitalized for three weeks and finally recovered. Another patient developed paralysis of her legs from Guillain-Barre syndrome. Fortunately, she recovered after a prolonged hospital stay. Both patients had received the Swine Flu vaccine three weeks previously.

What we learned from this episode was that instead of the flu killing millions of people, it claimed one life, while the vaccine turned out to be the real danger. In the end, it cost the United States government $3.5 billion in damages to some four thousand vaccine-injured Americans. So much for the CDC's intensive vaccination program.

The intrusion of the government over the Swine Flu scare reminded me of what I had observed in Ecuador and Puerto Rico. International organizations appeared more interested in reducing the population in these countries than promoting authentic economic development. The United States Agency for International Development (USAID) provided $722 million for population program assistance from 1965 to 1975. Puerto Rico achieved the highest sterilization rate of any country in the world with some 35% of the women of childbearing age being sterilized. India weighed in at 5% percent, and Pakistan at 3%. These public sterilization programs were propelled by an intense political propaganda campaign, which led people to believe that women in crisis and the high rate of unemployment were due to an increase in population. It should be noted that the United States paid for 90% of these sterilizations. Government intervention in health care means eliminating disease by eliminating people. Sterilization, contraception, abortion, and euthanasia are the "treatment" social planners have in mind when they move into an impoverished region.

The private practice of medicine is a time-honored, one-to-one relationship that serves the best interest of patients. Since its inception, the Association of American Physicians and Surgeons has had as its mission the protection of the private, patient-physician relationship. "We will identify and oppose any government or insurance company action that would cause a breach in this personal interaction. Any time an authoritarian entity would cause a physician to act against his own conscience, it must be opposed."[25]

History bears witness to the wisdom of the above ideal. One example is the story of Herman Niels Bundesen, M.D. As Health Commissioner of Chicago in 1930, Bundesen worked closely with the local board of health and the private physicians of the Chicago Medical Society to overcome food borne illnesses such as amebic dysentery and tuberculosis through the sterilization of milk. He spearheaded the great movement toward the prevention of neonatal death. He believed that an infant life saved was worth much, not only in terms of the amount of years an infant might live, but also in the measure of his or her contribution to the life of the human race.[26] In 1934, Bundesen introduced the Grade A Pasteurization Milk Ordinance and made it clear that no one would interfere with the passage of this bill. As a result of the ordinance, Chicago's milk supply achieved safe and wholesome standards. The following year, a 16% reduction in infant mortality proved the wisdom of Bundesen's plan.

The American Medical Association's *Code of Medical Ethics* has been the authoritative ethics guide for practicing physicians since the mid-1800s. The *Code* expresses the enduring values of medicine as a profession. As a statement of the values to which physicians commit themselves

[25] Alieta Eck, M.D., "Saving Private Practice." Journal of American Physicians and Surgeons. Volume 17. No. 3. Fall 2012. Available at *www.jpands.org/vol17no3/eck.pdf.*
[26] Bundesen, N. *Progress in the Prevention of Needless Neonatal Death.* Report of the Chicago Health Department, 1951.

individually and collectively, the *Code* is a standard of practice for the medical community. It defines medicine's integrity and the source of the profession's authority to self-regulate.

At the same time, the *Code of Medical Ethics*, like the United States Constitution, is a living document that evolves with a changing world. New discoveries in medicine and innovations in treatment raise questions about the profession's core values as they apply in physicians' day-to-day practice. The *Code* links theory and practice, ethical principles with real world dilemmas in the care of patients. Could the values of a medical staff or hospital conflict with the values of an individual patient or the family of a patient? Could they be at conflict with the faith of a patient or his or her family?

When the *Code* came into being, a mostly shared value system existed between medical practitioners and the communities in which and for which they practiced. This value system suffered a gradual dissolution as President Lyndon B. Johnson's "Great Society" came into focus. The Great Society was based on several false notions, one of them being that government could solve all society's problems. A confusion of rights and privileges entered into the picture. The founders of this country had clearly set forth the inalienable rights of all people: life, liberty and the pursuit of happiness. One may enjoy these rights so long as he or she does not infringe on the same rights enjoyed by others. Privileges, on the other hand, in some way or another do infringe on another person's generosity.

It is a basic function of government to protect its people. This protection takes practical form in police and fire departments. It also gives rise to agencies that ensure the safety of our water and food, as well as keep guard over the spread of disease. Under the American system, citizens have a right to health care if and only if they can pay for it. Nobody has the right to the services of any professional individual or group simply because he wants it or desperately needs it. The very fact that someone needs certain services is proof that he had better respect the freedom, integrity, and rights of the people who provide them.

Many physicians, however, succumbed to the allurement of Medicare and Medicaid in 1965 without realizing that doing so necessarily weakened their defense against government intrusion. The reasoning ran thus: "Why not accept the government's payments in return for medical service to those who cannot pay for it?" Was it care for the poor or simple greed that brought down the walls? Either way, what followed was the erection of a welfare state that not only ended a golden age in medical practice but gradually eroded the doctor-patient relationship.

Fast-forward thirty years. Health care providers have adopted Hilary Clinton's motto "It takes a village to raise a child." They have stepped into the role of parents, assuming to themselves the task of monitoring and treating children and adolescents. They view parents as extraneous once a child has entered adolescence. Teenage girls may gain access to contraceptives and treatment for sexually transmitted diseases without parental knowledge or consent. Fewer than half of the states in our country require parental consent for abortion. Doctors' offices systematically isolate adolescents from their parents. A recent article on adolescent health care in *American Family Physician Magazine* emphasized the importance of excluding parents from adolescent health care decision in order to foster more effective communication between physicians and adolescent patients. After reading a firestorm of criticism of the article by parents, a lone physician responded:

> As a family medicine physician, I see children, teens, and adults. Parents . . . we don't want to get your child alone to corrupt them, teach them not to trust you, slap them around or anything else. We are taught to do this to capture at risk children. We are trying to catch the child who is being beaten by their mother and is afraid to say. We are trying to catch the child who's scared to say that they are being sexually abused by their uncle but won't say that in front of their dad. We have been given the task of protecting children who are not otherwise protected, and catching those at risk.[27]

Clearly, this doctor is misguided in regard to his goals as a medical professional. Doctors do not have the task of protecting children. The consequence of believing that they

---

[27] Peter Ham, MD, and Claudia Allen, PhD, "Adolescent Health Screening and Counseling," University of Virginia, Charlottesville, Virginia, *American Family Physician*. 15:86 (2012): 1109-1116.

do shifts the responsibility for key decisions in regard to children from parents to doctors and, ultimately, to government agencies. Only parents have the right to form, educate, and make medical decisions for their children and adolescents. They may reach out to communities and other persons for support in doing so, but no entity, including the government, can trump parents' legitimate rights to decide what is best for their children.

Again, the assumption here is that parent's fail in their task and the government must step in and make everything right. Rather than improve and make available better instruments to *support* parents in their mission, the government seeks to remove from parents the right of discernment and choice in regard to their children. The logic here is similar to what I described above in regard to Puerto Rico's sterilization campaign: Get rid of the patient's disease by getting rid of the patient. Here, the logic is get rid of parent failures by getting rid of parents.

The loss of autonomy in medical practice has exceeded anything we could have imagined when I was an intern. From the federal level, we pass to the world level.

Eileen and I sat down at the kitchen table one night after the children were in bed and decided what action we could take to stop the erosion of the moral fiber of our country. So began our journey in defense of the unborn and our fight for religious freedom. The so-called "sexual revolution," the civil rights movement, the closing of Vatican Council II, and the Vietnam War aroused in us the conviction that we were facing a spiritual battle.

Fortunately, as Catholics, we were armed for this battle with the grace of sacramental life and certain teaching on the moral life. In his 1967 encyclical *Humanae vitae*, Pope Paul VI clearly laid out the trajectory of moral decline to such horrors.[28] He cautioned against four main problems that would arise if Catholic teaching on the regulation of births were ignored. First, he warned that the widespread use of contraception would lead to "conjugal infidelity and the general lowering of morality." Second, he foresaw that men would lose respect for women. A man would no longer care for a woman's "physical and psychological equilibrium" to the point that he would consider her "as a mere instrument of selfish enjoyment, and no longer as his respected and beloved companion." In other words, contraception might be marketed as liberating for women, when in reality the "beneficiaries" of birth control pills and devices would be men. Third, the Holy Father predicted that contraception would be a "dangerous weapon . . . in the hands of public authorities who take no heed of moral exigencies." In brief, contraception will end with conjugal life in the hands of the state:

> Who will prevent public authorities from favoring those contraceptive methods which they consider more effective? Should they regard this as necessary, they may even impose their use on everyone. It could well happen,

---

[28] The full text of *Humanae Vitae* is available at http://w2.vatican.va/content/paul-vi/en/encyclicals/documents/hf_p-vi_enc_25071968_humanae-vitae.html.

therefore, that when people, either individually or in family or social life, experience the inherent difficulties of the divine law and are determined to avoid them, they may give into the hands of public authorities the power to intervene in the most personal and intimate responsibility of husband and wife.[29]

One of the flaws in contemporary reasoning about contraception and abortion is the failure to see these evils in historical context. The truth is that eugenics – the desire to form a perfect race – did not cease after Hitler. On the contrary, it expanded into population control policies accepted at nearly every foreign aid discussion, leading to the massive export of contraceptives, abortion, and sterilization by the developed world to developing countries despite local moral and religious traditions. When Eileen and I visited the World Health Organization (WHO) in Geneva, Switzerland, we were greatly disturbed to learn that their objective in eliminating disease was a thinly disguised form of population warfare. Their aim, in essence, was to reduce the number of people in the world through contraception and abortion. Obviously, disease – as they understand it – refers to the body and not to the soul.

The final warning from Pope Paul VI was that contraception would mislead human beings into thinking that they have unlimited control over their own bodies, turning the

---

[29] Ibid.

human person into the object of his or her own power. At the heart of contraception is the assumption that fertility is an illness that much be cured, an infection that must be attacked and controlled in the same way that antibiotics attack bacteria. If fertility is an infection to be cured then what else could life in the womb be but a pathogen to be destroyed? In either case, a defining element of woman's identity – her potential for bearing new life – is recast as a weakness that elicits distrust and requires "treatment." Women become the object of the tools they rely on to ensure their liberation and defense from themselves, that is, their own bodies. Tragically, by their own choosing, they turn themselves into objects of use, rather than love.

Not all countries of the world have bought into the eugenics/abortion agenda. In 1983, history was made in Ireland – although the rest of the world chose to ignore the event. By popular vote, Ireland chose to stem the tide of abortion on demand that had claimed even Catholic Italy. Pro-life groups from the United States had been working with various Catholic medical and pro-life organizations in Ireland for several years prior to this historic vote. As of this writing, Ireland continues to resist any relaxing of her prohibition against abortion. Irish women who wish to kill their unborn Irish children must go to England to do so. It is difficult not to grasp the irony of the situation. After several centuries of oppression under English rule, having finally achieved independence from Britain, the Irish seek that country out for the annihilation of Irish babies. English doctors are only too happy to comply.

In 1981, our family was able to attend a conference sponsored by the World Federation of Doctors Who Respect Human Life. This conference, which planted the seeds that ultimately nourished the Irish Pro-Life movement, was hosted by Trinity College in Dublin. It was an enormously successful meeting attended by scientists and medical personnel from every major country of the world including some from behind the Iron Curtain. Dr. Herbert Ratner from Oak Park, Illinois, and the late Fr. Charles Corcoran, Fr. Paul Marx, and legal giants Congressman (IL) Henry Hyde, Dennis Horan, and the Surgeon General of the United States, C. Everett Koop, M.D., were also present. In 1982, Eileen and I welcomed two young Irish ladies who stayed with us for three days in order to learn the pit falls and problems that would confront them in the pro-life battle.

On September 7, 1983, a referendum to the Irish Constitution passed 841,233 to 415,136. In the words of the referendum, "the state acknowledges the right to life of the unborn and with due regard to the equal right to life of the mother, guarantees in its laws to respect, and so far as practical by its laws to defend and vindicate that right."[30] The rural areas where the socio-economic status was lower had a more favorable affirmative vote. The Prime Minister of the Republic, Gamet Fitzgerald, along with most part leaders, were against the referendum.

---

[30] Eighth Amendment of the Constitution Act, 1983, available at http://www.irishstatutebook.ie/eli/1983/ca/8/enacted/en/print.

I am proud that Eileen and I were able to assist in the protection of Irish women and babies – not to mention all of the other causes we have taken up over the years. Truth be told, however, our primary focus was on the souls under our own roof. Our primary vocation as parents required us to care for the care and education of our children. We did so collaboratively, drawing from our own faith and experiences, as well as awareness of the kinds of challenges that our children would face as adults.

Chapter Seven

The Fruitful Vine

> The Christian family constitutes a specific revelation and realization of ecclesial communion, and for this reason it can and should be called a *domestic church.* – Familiaris Consortio, #21

In the last view chapters, I focused on the gradual appearance of what St. John Paul II called "a culture of death." I would like to spend this chapter celebrating a culture of life, specifically, the life that my wife and I and are children had together. One of the first things you learn in the study of biology is that life resists entropy. Organic beings are a miracle in the universe because they exist and grow despite the inclination of all things to chaos. In the midst of many evils, life remains a perennial good. My wife and I were blessed with many children. Our home was full of life. It may not always be easy to have and raise a large family, but the "burdens" involved are light in comparison to the gift of every child. Children are, in fact, as the Church has proclaimed, the "crowning gift" of marriage.

How can you sum up the life of a family? How can you capture the joy and sorrow, the predictability and surprise, the tiny steps and the enormous leaps forward? A few years ago, I came across a book of quotes by the columnist Erma

Bombeck. One quote struck me as a very accurate description of family life as I had known it:

> We were a strange little band of characters trudging through life, sharing diseases and toothpaste, coveting one another's desserts, hiding shampoo, borrowing money, locking each other out of our rooms, inflicting pain and kissing to heal it in the same instant, loving, laughing, defending, and trying to figure out the common thread that bound us all together.[31]

This quote comes as close as may be possible to describing my cherished memories as a husband and father. I want to put weighty issues aside in this chapter and speak instead of the people who have made my life truly worthwhile. As with most memories, feeling is often stronger than details, and chronology may not be accurate.

The Sisters of the Cenacle had a retreat house just across the street from where we lived on Longwood Drive in Beverly. Their order followed Ignatius spirituality with its mission "to work for the transformation of the world by awakening and deepening faith."[32] Our children loved to visit the sisters in their religious surroundings. The girls, especially Maureen, Michelle, and Kathy, would wait on tables during

---

[31] Erma Bombeck, *The Ties That Bind...and Gag!* (New York, NY: Fawcett Books, 1987), 11.

[32] The sisters remain active today. See their website at https://www.cenaclesisters.org/chicago.

retreats and answer the phone. Even our ducks loved to waddle across the street and swim in their pond.

One day, Michelle ran into the house crying and blubbering something about a duck and a dog. Sure enough, Eileen and I ran outside to discover that the Cenacle's dog had decided to try fresh duck. The poor victim lay on its side, wounded and surrounded by all the neighborhood children. Another duck ran around in a circle, quacking hysterically. The perpetrator of the crime had already been propelled home, tail between his legs, driven by angry children throwing sticks and making cat calls.

We hastily fashioned a large carton for the duck and transferred him to the station wagon for the trip to the vet. Michelle covered him with my good golfing sweater. The neighborhood children, acting as paramedics, piled into the car. The healthy duck could not be left alone, so my wife placed him in a box next to his friend. The scene in the waiting room was unprecedented: two ducks in two boxes, quacking without ceasing, one wearing a golfing sweater, surrounded by crying children. The vet knew a real emergency when he saw one. He hastily sutured the wounded duck and let everyone know that the patient would survive. Crying turned to laughter on the drive home. In fact, the duck made a quick and complete recovery and was even able to participate in the 4th of July parade just a few days later. This parade also featured rabbits, many dogs, decorated bikes, and kids, kids, kids. To keep cars from careening through our streets, there were strategically placed toys spread out "obstacle course" fashion along the whole length of road.

By this point, God had blessed our family with seven children. One day, our two-year old twins Kevin and Kathleen decided to climb out of their beds and onto the garage roof. The windows had unwisely been left open. They could not resist the temptation! My wife and I were enjoying dinner with the other five children in our breakfast nook. It was our sixth wedding anniversary. Even Anne Kinnane, our family's very own Mary Poppins, was pleased with the tranquility of the evening.

Soft crying from outside disturbed our serenity. The premonition of a mother made my wife jump out of her chair and bolt to the driveway. There was Kevin lying motionless on the pavement. He must have walked right off the garage roof. We all gathered around him, praying out loud. I carried him into the house, asking God for just one more favor on that list that was always growing. Miraculously, Keven was totally unharmed by his fall. Meanwhile, his sister was still on the garage roof, watching the theatrics down below. Needless to say, we wasted no time in drawing her back into the house.

Such is life in a large family. You never know what each day will bring. With faith and courage and a good sense of humor, you face it all together.

My wife and I made the decision to keep our children as far away from television as possible. Hence, guitar, accordion, piano, and organ lessons kept the kids busy for most of the week until Saturday morning. If only they had had school on that day!

Not only were we faced with the challenges of a large family, there was also life in Chicago to keep us on our toes.

Once, while the family was away, a bomb blew out the door of a union official's home across the street. Thanks to underworld involvement, the restaurant down the street also had its moment with a planted bomb. Our home was burglarized with us in it. These happenings were part and parcel of living in Chicago. We just grinned and bore it.

My life was full between home and work. Daily rounds at two hospitals and a session at the office allowed me to observe situations unique to the medical profession. Death, birth, tragedies, and joys occurred with the variety and symmetry of a glimpse through a kaleidoscope. At a certain point, I relinquished by consultant privileges at Oak Forest County, controlled by Cook County Hospital, because of the distance and time involved. Documentation of medical meetings, rotation of credential and tissue committee members, as well as medical staff officers, were done yearly. This turnover was good for the patients, the hospital, and the community. Personal favors could then be kept to a minimum. It would be nice if the same rule applied to elected officials. It has been said that a government which governs least, governs best. Occupying their offices for several years running allows elected officials to create dynasties and fill their own coffers for the next election, thereby keeping taxpayers at their mercy.

Thanks to the practice of our Catholic faith, my memories of this period are closely associated with baptisms, first communions, confirmations, and the practices or festivities surrounding major holidays such as Christmas and Easter. Participation in Sunday Mass started the night before with everyone retiring early. I, too, called it a day sooner than later, returning from the hospital by noon or one o'clock, just in time to load all the children in the car and head out to cheer for whichever child was in Junior Pony or Little League or football midgets – not to mention the cheerleaders.

If the snow was right, my wife and I would take the teenagers skiing in Wilmont on Friday afternoons after school. Not just our teenagers, either. We hired a bus for the teenage club. Along with other parents acting as chaperones, we would occupy the back of the bus, watching our teenagers closely from a distance.

One particular ski trip looms large in my recollections. The day began in ordinary enough fashion. Terry Whalen, the best football player on the varsity team, led the pack up the ski mountain. We, the chaperones, had a beautiful view of the ski lift and ski run from the picture window in the lodge. What could be more perfect? My wife and I and the Pierces sat down to a snack, knowing that our forty or so teenagers had rented their equipment and were now slowly pouring out to the lifts.

Many beginners and a few "hot dogs" peppered the ski run. Terry Whalen toddled a little at the top of the run, but he was determined to lead the formation to the bottom. With the speed of an instructor, he was down the run, with his poles making a circular motion and his legs frozen in a perfect "I" formation. His body, however, swayed forward and backward, and we chaperones, watching in alarm, knew that disaster was imminent. Apparently, so did Terry. Barreling at the speed of light downward, he managed to avoid the crowd, opting instead to aim for a large tree to buffer his fall. We learned later that Terry had never been on skis before!

A rescue team responded quickly to Terry's fall. We all hurried to the emergency area to discover that he had fractured his femur. To our great relief, close examination revealed no other injuries. He must have been a solid specimen because I am sure that no other person could have weathered that collision at the speed he was traveling. My wife rode the fifty miles back with Terry in the ambulance to St. Francis Hospital while the rest of us followed later in the bus. He was courageous all the way back, even though the pain was excruciating. The right leg was splinted well, but every little motion of the speeding ambulance brought silent tears to his eyes. The hospital staff placed him in the orthopedic service under the care of Dr. Schneider. I was able to visit him daily to be sure he was all right.

Considering the many changes we were witnessing in culture, Eileen and I decided that it would be good for our children to have a greater sense of their religious and cultural heritage. If the children could see the places where their ancestors had lived and make pilgrimage to the places that marked the mysteries of their Catholic faith, they would not be so easily swayed by the notion of "change for change's sake." Our three-week trip came together quickly. The first port of call would be Ireland, followed by England, and finally, Rome. We found boarding for the dog and gave our house over to my wife's parents for safe keeping. Passports were put in order and the buddy system set in place. We were ready.

We slept all the way to Shannon airport on our Aer Lingus flight. Mr. McLaughlin had two cars waiting for us upon our arrival. Five people were to ride in each car. I would drive one car with the four boys (Bobby, Jackie, Brian, and Kevin), while Mr. McLaughlin would take the other car with Eileen, Maureen, Michelle, Kathleen, and Mary. The girls had the better deal since Mr. McLaughlin had many an interesting tale to tell them as we traveled from hamlet to hamlet. The plan was to drive from Limerick on the west coast down to the Ring of Kerry and then up to Dublin and across from there to England.

From Shannon Airport we drove through Limerick to Dromoland Castle in County Clare. We found the quaint shops and narrow streets to be like those in the eastern United States. The stone walls lining the road were new for us. Kathy recognized the tinkers from the movie "Lassie Come Home." They are Irish gypsies who cruise through the towns in caravans of brightly covered horse-drawn wagons. The children were quick to pick up physical characteristics they had seen in the children of Irish immigrants back home. As we drove, they would shout out that that man was Mr. Murphy on Artesian Street or that woman was Mrs. Malone who taught at their school. There were striking resemblances for almost everyone we knew back home.

In some areas, we saw evidence and heard accounts of the potato famine that had driven so many Irish to the United States in the 19th century. These stories were bittersweet for us since the famine was what brought our ancestors to a new life in a new country – our country. I took the occasion to explain to Brian that good can result from evil, but evil can never result from good. He understood. Maureen wanted to know why we didn't have the Stations of the Cross along the roads in Chicago. Her mother suggested that the reason may be the Stations in the churches are hardly used – why put any along the roads?

We journeyed back to Limerick where we visited a relative of one of our neighbors back home, the Kellehers. The poor woman was crippled with arthritis, so we talked to her in her bedroom. She told us she had been waiting six months to get into a hospital.

The Sisters of the Little Company of Mary Hospital in Evergreen Park, Illinois, had a hospital in Ireland that I wished to visit. It was over one hundred and fifty years old and still fairly busy for an Irish hospital. Compared to my experiences in Chicago's hospitals, however, I found the pace pleasingly slow.

My deceased father's cousin still lived in Drogheda, just north of Dublin. We were able to have a cup of tea with them. Mr. Dolehide had a nose like my father's, and his expressions were similar. He said his daughter had joined the nursing Cabrini sisters in Chicago. As we journeyed through the narrow streets of Drogheda, we passed a beautiful church in the center of town. We all ascended the steep steps and went inside. One of the children found a shrine on the left side of the altar. The famous bishop, Oliver Plunkett, was entombed there, his head enclosed in glass. He had been sent to England by Cromwell, where he was dragged through the streets after serving many months in jail and then beheaded and quartered.

We said good-bye to Mr. McLaughlin and thanked him for the six days of sightseeing. We looked like a caravan of gypsies, each child and adult with two suitcases walking up to the ferry just south of Dublin that would take us to England across the Irish Channel. The trip took several hours. Running from the boat to train to cab, we finally landed in the metropolis of London. It was the fourth of July, so we had our own little celebration in the streets behind our hotel. I didn't know that the older boys had brought some fireworks and sparklers with them.

Our stay in London was brief. While the family enjoyed the beaches of Brighton, I attended an international meeting on internal medicine. Cook Travel in London came up with the perfect package tour for us: London to Rome, and then back through London to Dublin and home.

The train to Rome was an experience I will never forget. First of all, it was very crowded. We had to distribute the children as well as we could in various berths. To tell the truth, we lost them in the evenings when we couldn't figure out the numbering system. We just hoped and prayed that the buddy system would keep everyone together. Language was a challenge, too, as we traveled through France and Italy, especially when it concerned the train schedule. Whenever I heard a car unhitching in the middle of the night, I feared one or more of my children were speeding toward Switzerland or Spain. At one point, with no one around us speaking English, we decided to get off the train as it backed into the station. This turned out only to be a water-filling stop. Right about the time we figured this out, the train was moving out of the station. We had to run quickly to catch the last car. It was a sight to behold: ten people, each with two bags, running for the last car. The Italians on the train hung out the windows with their elbows flexed, not concerned in the least by the distress of their fellow passengers. I had the impression they were making bets on whether or not we would all make it. My heart sank as little Mary stopped running and just sat on her baggage crying. I threw my baggage on the platform, scooped her up in my arms, and with my last bit of strength, put my left arm through both straps of her luggage, all the while taking giant steps toward the moving car, cheered on by the other eight members of our family packed together on the rear platform. I made it, but I would have pulled the emergency cord with my teeth if I could have found it, I was so upset.

We definitely did not travel in style. Every morning, I tallied our money and decided that we should only eat breakfast until we got to Rome. The children would take the rolls and butter and jelly back to our railroad car, and we would break some of it out at noon time and again for supper, making a nice little picnic scene as we ate together in one of the berths.

All the travails of travel were worth it once we pulled into the Eternal City. Here stood material evidence that the Catholic Church was alive and well after twenty centuries. Christ had told Peter, "On this Rock I will build my Church, and the gates of hell shall not prevail against it." Through the centuries, kings, armies, theologians, heretical bishops, and even large numbers of the people of Europe had attempted to destroy this divinely instituted Church. As we crossed the threshold of St. Peter's, I told the children that this was the largest church in Christendom. Even the finger on Bernini's statue of St. Peter, I pointed out to them, was six feet long. We marveled at the massive altar. We were fortunate to see Michelangelo's Pieta before it was stricken two years later by a man wielding a hatchet.

In this chapter, I have recalled only a few of the memories dear to my heart. There are so many stories to tell, but most will have to be passed on through the oral tradition of our family long after I am gone. In this life, I was blessed with a holy wife and children about whom I can feel justifiably proud. It gives me great satisfaction to know that the vine Eileen and I planted and tended with such care has turned out to be so fruitful.

Chapter Eight

The Desensitization of a Generation

"Parents must teach their children to avoid the
compromising and degrading influences which
threaten human societies" (CCC 2224)

It is difficult to imagine today, but there was a time when procured abortion and assisted suicide were not options. Though these practices have always been with us, long-standing tradition did not tolerate them or accord them official approval. It was a given of human societies that no one had the right to terminate a human life once begun or in its final stages. The gift of life came from God; it belonged only to God to call that life back when the time had come. Hence, for some, the legalization of abortion and the public approval accorded euthanasia seemed to come out of nowhere. Overnight, the power of life and death landed in the hands of legislators and judges, while the medical profession, traditionally dedicated to doing no harm, could kill as well as heal.

The truth, however, is that the shift from a culture of life to a culture of death did not happen quickly or spontaneously. On the contrary, the early years of the twentieth century saw a concentrated effort on the part of many to advance an agenda that would overturn traditional values in an effort to create "a new world order." Those engaged in this effort understood that the public had to be prepared or "primed," if you will, to accept notions that conscience and traditional cultures rejected. The goal of this preparatory work was "desensitization," that is, the dulling of thought and feeling in the face of a moral decision. The secret to desensitization was confusion and doubt. If it could be shown that there are no absolute moral rules and no act is intrinsically right or wrong in itself, but rather, dependent on intentions and circumstances, then the door would be open for anything.

As a physician, I had a front row seat to the move from a culture of life to a culture of death. I watched the creeping chill of death take over my profession. At first, there will little indications that touched on the nature of medical care. The world had changed, it was argued, and medicine had to change with it. I don't remember when I first noticed a change in the atmosphere. Like most people, I assumed that the fundamental values would always be fundamental, and that I could count on my government and my Church to protect them. Little by little, I felt the ground of this certainty crumble beneath my feet. As it turned out, the shift in my profession's values was only one half of the equation. At home, too, as my wife and I strove to raise children of faith and virtue, I came to realize that nothing could be taken for granted. As parents, Eileen and I had to remain vigilant about the content of our children's education. We had to assume roles in our schools and churches that we had never envisioned for ourselves.

Let's begin first with the larger picture of societal change. Looking back, it is not difficult to discern the stages of desensitization that followed one upon the other from the early years of the 20th century onward. First, the foundations of traditional morality were put in question. Specific moral acts were cast in a new light in such a way that what had seemed certain now appeared uncertain. Exceptions to law and custom were allowed – out of compassion, of course. One should, for example, permit divorce or birth control in "special" cases. Horrible accounts of abused wives and mothers moved the general public to re-evaluate the permanence of the marriage bond and the ultimate meaning of sexual intercourse.

The consequence of a blurring in moral boundaries was particularly evident in the healing professions, both spiritual and physical. A flawed sentimentality shaped the perception of and response to human needs. An amazing shift occurred. Rather than finding ways to assist people in the living of the moral law, doctors, nurses, priests and ministers, sought to downplay heroic action by eliminating the situation that called for it. Married couples in crisis could opt for divorce; the discipline of responsible sexual intimacy could be side-stepped by birth control; inconvenient or unwanted pregnancies could be terminated by abortion. Easy solutions took the place of the hard path of moral uprightness and sacrifice.

How do I describe the response of my heart and conscience to colleagues who perceived the moral crisis of a patient as a mere question of practicality? Americans are famous for the philosophy of pragmatisms, namely, the notion that the only really moral answer to a problem is the one that gets the most useful results. Such thinking has enabled us to conquer the northern continent and put a man on the moon. It is completely unsuitable for moral judgements that concern life and death, family, and the duties human beings owe to each other. At first, in conversations with patients and colleagues, I had the impression that a kind of moral confusion had fallen upon us all. Eventually, I understood that there was no confusion. A new value system was in place, the principles of which became unquestionable.

The unkindest cut of all, however, was the one that came from my fellow Christians. It became the "in" thing for the Catholic Church, for example, to look like it was joining the modern world. The media assisted in the uprooting of traditional Christian teaching by flooding every possible outlet – newspaper, magazines, radio, motion pictures – with the opinions of young, well-meaning priests and ministers who represented a new, enlightened approach to human suffering – a kinder, gentler, more "Christian" response to the needs of women and children. A world of values turned upside down, and what had been wrong gradually became right. One technique of the media was to replace certain wrongs with other wrongs in the public mind. The Vietnam War, environmental issues, poverty, hunger – these evils grew larger as moral issues involving individual decisions – divorce, contraception, and abortion – grew smaller.

A change in culture requires a change in the way youth are prepared to live in that culture. Thanks to the Pill and a new era of sexual freedom, sex-related social problems escalated. Schools were called upon to address these problems by developing sex education programs that would ensure young people understood the facts of life, the transmission of sexual disease, and the methods of preventing pregnancy. At first, there was opposition. Sex education had always taken place within the family; it was considered the right and duty of parents to educate their children about sex in a way they saw fit. Little by little, however, the idea acquired momentum. School officials who oversaw the implementation of sex education programs embraced their work with a crusading passion, addressing dissent with a superior and moralistic tone.

Chicago holds a special place in the history of public, sex education programs. The "Chicago controversy," as it was called, laid out the themes that were to characterize the politics of sex education all over the United States over the next few years. Both supporters and opponents agreed that promiscuity among teens was a problem. However, where supporters felt that knowledge about sexuality and reproduction would lead young people toward responsible behavior, opponents argued that any information about sexuality, no matter how well-intended, would corrupt students' minds and bring about an increase in promiscuity. These notions continue at the center of sex education discussions to this day.

The contest over sex education in the classroom was indicative of an even deeper cultural shift, namely, the movement from parent-controlled family life to state-controlled family life. Up until the 20th century, state law, policies, and institutions deferred to parents as the primary educators and caretakers of their children. It was a given of our society that parents knew what was best for their children – not the state. Sometime in the 1970s, subtle suggestions began to appear in the media that parents may not be the best guardians of their children. Reporting on domestic and child abuse gradually formed in the public mind the impression that parents could be the enemies of their children's well-being. Government stepped into the void created by this media blitz, becoming in very truth a "nanny state" that could intervene in areas traditionally left to parents. The worst of it, however, was that along with government control came the values of an entirely secular, materialistic culture. These values were glaringly apparent in sex education materials that reduced sex to a mere bodily function.

Eileen and I experienced firsthand how parents were treated if they dared question the aims and methods of sex education programs. The insensitivity and insult that parents were accorded in such instances was almost diabolical. Sad to say, we did not suffer at the hands of a secular school board where we would have anticipated a difference in values. No, we were scorned by our own.

At first, my Eileen and I watched with concern, but some detachment, what was happening in public education. Since our own children were in Catholic schools, we felt distant from the issue. Catholic schools followed a traditional teaching on the sex education of children. This teaching was not something out-of-date or medieval. Throughout the 20th century, popes and councils addressed the issue in no uncertain terms. Sex education is to be "prudent and positive." It is the responsibility of parents in the home and on an individual basis. It holds up the virtue of chastity, that is, self-control in regard to sexual activity. Chastity protects the dignity of persons through the regulation of the passions and the use of sex only within marriage. The Second Vatican Council stated clearly: "Especially in the heart of their own families, young people should be aptly and seasonably instructed about the dignity, duty, and expression of married love."[33]

Eileen and I assumed our responsibility as Catholic parents to see to the sex education of our children as the Church directed. We did not expect such instruction to take place at school. In fact, into the late sixties, Church authorities took a dim view of sex education in the classroom. When Chicago became the first major city to implement sex education in high school in 1913, the diocese led a powerful attack on the program and helped secure the resignation of its sponsor, Ella Flagg Young, the superintendent of schools.

By the time Eileen and I had children in the Catholic school system, however, a new spirit of "assimilation" had entered into Diocesan policies. The goal was to show that the Church was up-to-date and standing shoulder to shoulder with

---

[33] Vatican Council II, *Gaudium et Spes*, #49.

secular programs addressing current social issues. As a result of this philosophy, the Catholic Church in Chicago implemented a sex education program.

On one occasion, Eileen and I were asked by the local parish school board to review a series of books called *Becoming a Person*. This series was put out by the Roman Catholic Cana Conference Sex Education Pilot Project of Chicago. I found problems with the curriculum proposed by this series. The inside cover revealed that most of the material had come from the American School Health Association – a non-Catholic entity. This fact suggested that secular values were to take pride of place over Catholic teaching. Sure enough, nowhere in the text was there mention of God, sin, religion, conscience, or anything even remotely resembling a Christian standard of morality in regard to human sexuality. But even at the secular level, the series was deficient. As a parent of a large family, well versed with the trajectory from childhood to pubescence, I found the material covered not age appropriate and potentially damaging to a child who was not ready for it.

As a parent and physician, I was ready to make a public presentation of my concerns under the auspices of the Cana Conference. The author of the series, a priest, blocked my efforts to do so. There were, however, serious issues to be addressed. For one thing, I suspected that the author had not been entirely truthful. He wrote that during his assignment at St. Anne's Hospital in Chicago, a young girl had almost hemorrhaged to death from her first menstrual period. Her mother, he stated, had not prepared her for menstruation.

Never in my thirty years of practicing internal medicine had I ever witnessed such a situation. It was, in my opinion, pure fiction and served only to justify – through shock tactics – the existence of the series. In fact, whenever I spoke to groups about sex education in the classroom, I would mention this distortion of fact as an example of a "wedge in the door."

On one occasion, I met with St. Walter's school board chairman and explained to him the need for more language and science courses in grade school. I took the opportunity to explain that sex education not only thwarted children's intellectual and moral development, but also damaged what psychologists have called the "latency" period of child sexual awareness. This period extends from ages six to fifteen when a child's physical development lags behind mental development. During this period, children have difficulty comprehending the biological development of a baby within a human body. Many studies have shown that classroom instruction of children in the latency period is dehumanizing and leads to neurosis.

Eileen and I had already shared our belief that sex education classes should be extracurricular and not part of the required curriculum. The board agreed, and we took on the task of presenting the classes. We chose evenings and asked parents to accompany their children. In this way, no child would be considered a victim of protective parents if he did not attend the sessions. Boys were separated from girls in order to protect the modesty of each. For materials, we made use of Father Rattemai's books and slides. Moreover, the entire course took six sessions, as opposed to one session of each for eight years as proposed in the series. We found that our efforts worked very well. The diocese, however, did not share our enthusiasm. The powers-that-be were upset that our school had not purchased "their" approved series.

One evening, the Chicago Archdiocese school board sent the head of the school system, a priest, to our parish to address parents on the matter. It was an early spring evening during Lent, when the parish really was more interested in preparing for retreats, days of recollection, and the greatest feast day in the Church: Easter Sunday. The good Dominican sisters in their starched and pleated white habits occupied the first row. The pastor, assistant pastor, and Sister Henry Marie, O.P., occupied the stage with the lecturer. The audience consisted of parents who were making great sacrifices to send their children to a parochial school.

The lecturer placated his audience with one joke after another about the Chicago White Sox and Cubs baseball teams. I waited until the question and answer period to have my say. As the father of eight children, I thanked God for an educational system that cared for my children's spiritual growth, as well as their educational advancement. I thanked Father Peterson and the priests and sisters who were devoting their lives to serving others. We could never repay parishioners their charity. I then rebuked our lecturer and the Archdiocesan School Board for betraying the trust of thousands of parents by presenting a program in human sexuality based on a value system contrary to the Ten Commandments. I reminded him also that sex education outside of the family is a violation of parental rights, an attack on a child's innocence, and a rejection of the Church's own guidelines for the proper education and formation of children in human sexuality. I made my objection absolutely clear: *Becoming a Person* was a series of books intended to cast into doubt the value system of parents. How else were we to understand questions such as "Does your mother become angry if your father stays out late?" "Does your mother or father scold you if you eat candy before dinner?" Such questions have nothing to do with sex education. They are, rather, an attack on parental authority. They drive a wedge between parents and their children – a clear violation of the commandment to "honor your father and your mother."

I slowly and methodically explained the difference between formal and informal education. I also expressed concern about how some Catholic schools were readily abandoning a Catholic education in favor of the curriculums in public schools. This fact was nowhere more evident than in the way they had caved in to liberal pressure to include sex education programs. A precedent was being set to eliminate traditional Catholic values and teaching from Catholic schools. Many bishops were persuaded to permit and even recommend sex education in the formal classroom setting.

But what disturbed me the most, I noted, was the assumption that parents were not doing their job of teaching sexuality to their children. It was this assumption that led the Archdiocese of Chicago to insist that lay teachers who had taken a short course on sex education were more qualified. As I reflected on this, I referred to two different books. The first, *The Hamlets of Laos* by Dr. Tom Dooley, describes a

Christian teacher whose tongue was pulled out by Communist soldiers for preaching the Word of God to children. It tells of children who had bamboo sticks thrust into their ears so that they could never again hear the Word of God. The second book was Aldous Huxley's prophetic *Brave New World*. In this fictional account of the future, parental involvement with offspring is considered primitive and quaint. A central government takes full control of raising children, and the concept of "family" utterly disappears.

Our lecturer was clearly annoyed with me as I questioned what made a good teacher of sex education. Is it a young, single person just out of college, whose morals are different from ours? Many of these young adults were my patients through the years. Some were struggling with same sex attraction, others on drugs, and many on birth control. Did I wish these people to teach their interpretations of the Ten Commandments to my children?

Why, I asked, had the peace sign so often replaced the cross in the classroom? Many young teachers, caught up in the peace movement of the day, had no concept of the historical meaning of the peace sign. They wore it proudly around their necks or on shirts and sweatshirts. In medieval paintings of the devil, the peace sign – called "Nero's Cross" – was always plainly visible in the pupil of his eyes. Both arms of the Christian were broken. The swastika of the Nazis was a form of the peace sign. The peace sign was placed over the graves of Hitler's SS troops who died in action in World War II. The very same men had pulled Jewish children away from their parents, sending the latter and many times the former to the gas chambers of the concentration camps. We had won the war – or had we? Whose values had triumphed?

Several weeks later, I learned that our courageous school board had upheld its convictions. They decided that the series *Becoming a Person* was not in the best interest of our school children and voted it down. Later, the bishops found this series to be very inadequate. The controversy surrounding it disappeared from sight, only to be replaced by controversies over other similar series. And the fight goes on.

My ordeal with the Archdiocesan school board gained me a local reputation as an opponent of sex education. This could not have been further from the truth, as is evident in the efforts Eileen and I put in to offering a sex education curriculum after school. Nevertheless, I was invited to debate proponents of "humanistic" sex education in the various school districts, public and private, throughout Chicago land. As a member of the school board, and later as a trustee at an exclusive private school on the south side of Chicago, I was delighted to discover that their curriculum was in its appropriate place, in the science of biology as a health course.

My story is just one small indication of how education systems were becoming more and more a tool of the state. Catholic leadership in the United States, sadly, bought into many parts of the new curriculum. The Church itself, however, remained clear in her teaching on human sexuality. The 1975 *Vatican Declaration on Sexual Ethics* states: "There are many people today who, being confronted with so many widespread opinions opposed to the teaching which they received from the Church, have come to wonder what they must now hold as true. The Church cannot remain indifferent to the confusion of minds and relaxation of morals."[34]

The Church followed through on this statement with a precise explanation – a summary, really – of what she has perennially held to be true about human sexuality. This teaching has been repeated many times since. In the face of a world gone mad, the Church has remained the rock that Our Lord promised it would be.

Not so the law of the United States. At first, there was resistance. Since the 1920s, the Supreme Court had acknowledged the right of parents to control the education and upbringing of their children, with some opt-out policies. Senator Hatch put forth a U.S. Bill that would force schools to allow parents to review objectionable materials. In recent year, however, the tide has turned almost entirely against parental control and responsibility. The concerns of parents about what their children are learning have been downplayed as government bureaucrats, public school teachers, and even healthcare providers take on more and more control of the curriculum. Parents are considered, at best, ineffective, and, at worst, ignorant and irresponsible. It is assumed that the State and the "experts" know better how to form future generations.

Public education is one thing, but how could the Catholic school system become so corrupted? I have noted already that Catholic leadership made a deliberate decision to

---

[34] *Personae humanae* (Declaration on Certain Problems of Sexual Ethics). 29 December 1975. *AAS* 68 (1976): 77-96. Found in *Vatican Council II: More Post-Conciliar Documents*, ed. Austin Flannery, O.P. (Collegeville: The Liturgical Press, 1982), 486-499.

imitate and even adopt the curricula of public schools. This decision reflected a belief in certain current theories of human psychology. Dr. William Coulson, self-admitted architect of the destruction of religious orders, offers us a clue as to how psychology brought about also the end of traditional Catholic education. In response to a question about the negative results of "Feeling Therapy," which resulted in forced abortions by one of Coulson's spin-off groups, he answered:

> Humanistic psycho-therapy, the kind that has virtually taken over the Church in America, and dominates so many forms of aberrant education like sex education, and drug education, holds that the most important source of authority is within you, that you must listen to yourself. Well, if you have a baby you're carrying under your heart, get rid of it. Women who came into the Center for Feeling Therapy were forced to give them up for adoption. The only person who was allowed to have a baby, in an eerie preview of David Koresh, was the principal founder of the institution. All the other babies were killed, or sent away, in the name of getting in touch with the imperial *self*. . .[35]

When asked about his experience with sex education, Coulson admitted that he pulled his own kids out of the Catholic

---

[35] Excerpted from the article "Repentant Psychologist: How I Wrecked the I. H. M. Nuns" in *The Latin Mass, Chronical of Catholic Reform*, 1994.

schools when they "began to be corrupted" even when he was still a Rogerian psychologist. "The kids would get an experiential education if they stayed in that setting; they would not get a Catholic education."[36]

What did Coulson mean by "experiential education"? He explained:

> If you park a group of kids in a circle to talk about their sexual experiences, who's going to have the most interesting stories to tell? The most experienced child. Where is the direction of influence going to run? It's going to run – and the research confirms this again and again – it's going to run from the experienced to the inexperienced. The net outcome of sex education . . . is more sexual experience.[37]

It is one thing for a person outside of the system to criticize it; it is another for someone from *within* the system to do so. Coulson speaks as one of the architects and proponents of a new approach to human education, including sex education. Having seen the errors of his ideas and their tragic outcome, he has a great deal to tell us. His own contrite admission helps us to understand the ravages done to children by the so-called "professionals."

In this chapter, I have sought to integrate two stories. On the one hand, the surrounding culture was living out a new scale of values that impacted on every aspect of human life.

---

[36] Available at https://www.ewtn.com/library/PRIESTS/COULSON.TXT.
[37] Ibid.

On the other hand, there were people like Eileen and me, just ordinary working people, raising families and trying to pass on to their children their own values. Perhaps these times are unique for precisely this reality: For the first time in history, a battle raged between a powerful and "enlightened" few determined to change the fabric of reality, and a few keen-sighted people committed to the fundamental and irrevocable truths of the human condition expressed in Christian belief. As parents, Eileen and I had to operate at two levels all the time, keeping an eye on government and media while also vigilantly protecting our children at school and in their everyday contact with others outside of our home. The forces of culture were arrayed against us, but the power of faith and the grace of Divine Providence were on our side. When I look at our children today, and their children, I feel that our efforts were blessed.

Chapter Nine

Faith and Healing

*For those with faith, no explanation is
necessary. For those without faith, no
explanation is possible. - St. Thomas Aquinas*

I would like to devote this chapter to the ways in which
divine grace influences the living body. I would like to show,
based on my experiences as a physician, how important faith
is to the medical practitioner and how miracles, far from being
flights of fancy, are realistic possibilities.

For Christians, physical healing in this life bears
witness to the ultimate healing from all pain and death in the
coming of God's kingdom. Interestingly, Old Testament
miracles were very grand in scale: the parting of the Red Sea,
for example, or the Pillar of Fire that accompanied the
Israelites on their journey. The miracles of the New
Testament, on the other hand, were smaller, more personal
manifestations of God's power. Jesus cast out demons, healed
the sick, and raised the dead. He commanded his disciples to
do the same. The mission of the Christian physician is to
imitate Jesus as healer. The power of healing came from
Jesus' divinity. The Christian physician, through his study and

training, becomes a channel of that same healing power – especially if he conducts his ministry with faith and prayer.

Right away, I can imagine the objections raised by those whose faith is in science. But the long tradition of human wisdom has always maintained the existence of a supernatural, invisible realm that is the source of everything we see. The laws governing nature did not originate from themselves, but were put in place by a divine intelligence. Physicians recognize this intelligence by the efforts they have made to learn nature's laws; they give homage to it in the healing work they accomplish by obeying it.

Let's start by separating two kinds of believers. There are those whose faith is an emotional affair only, without any rational content. Such people give a bad name to those who believe in spirit and truth. True faith is an intellectual gift that does not replace the intellect. On the contrary, it enlightens understanding, making its gaze more perceptive and discerning. It may or may not be accompanied by feelings, but its certainty does not depend on them. In the words of the Savior, "You should know the truth, and the truth shall set you free" (John 8:32).

What does this have to do with miracles? In the first place, people of true faith are not gullible types who readily accept any suggestion. They believe in miracles, but they don't go chasing after them. When they hear tell of a "miracle," they allow it to be tested by experts and theologians before they give their assent. Believers are, in fact, dubious when faced with reports of supernatural events. They admit that there is a great deal about the natural world that cannot be understood. They acknowledge that the human mind is complex and mysterious and that many things that pass for "supernatural" have more to do with the workings of the human mind than the workings of God. Nonetheless, believers do not deny the possibility of miracles. Faith in God, spirits, and a supernatural realm leaves them open to explanations that go beyond this world and the limited knowledge of human beings. For Christian believers, the two greatest miracles of all time were the Incarnation and the Resurrection. How can anyone explain God becoming a man and then, after dying as a man, rising again from the dead? For Christians, these events are historical facts and miracles at the same time.

And miracles do happen. Scientists may scoff at the notion, but scientists themselves have often been stumped by events they cannot explain. Some choose to believe that what we call a "miracle" simply lacks an explanation right now. Someday, science will have the answer. Other scientists, however, accept that the understanding of the material world is not entirely open to human beings. There is an impenetrable mystery at the heart of matter and physical processes. Without attempting to prove the existent of an immaterial realm, these honest scientists at least accept that some things are beyond explanation.

Catholic physicians, as physicians, are trained in the scientific method. They deal with material facts just as their non-believing colleagues do. Yet, they remain open to the possibility of supernatural intervention as a real part of their practice. As Catholics, they also trust the Church to do her job of investigating and certifying extraordinary events before calling them "miracles." In fact, the Church does not use this word lightly. A long and careful process that often engages the investigation of non-believing experts as well as the testimony of non-believing witnesses must take place before the Church will designate an event miraculous. The most famous area of such inquiry in the Catholic Church is the process of canonization. For a man or woman to be recognized as a saint by the Church, at least one miraculous healing must be obtained through that person's intercession.

Another area over which the Church keeps careful watch is reported apparitions of Mary, Mother of Jesus. In recent years, the Church has been busy on this account. One could say that the Church has been busy because the Blessed Virgin has been busy. As the modern world has careened further from the path of truth, the Blessed Virgin has intervened with cautions, promises, and gifts.

The intervention of the Mother of God in modern history has been frequent and well documented. She has been busy crushing the head of the serpent by calling her children back to her Divine Son. In 1711, St. Louis de Montfort, the great troubadour of Mary, wrote that there would be a great return to Christ and the Church towards the end of human history. The many apparitions of the Blessed Virgin throughout the world have surely been a catalyst for this event. There is no space here to recount every instance in which she has touched individuals and communities in the two millennia of the Christian era. Let us consider only the most important of these interventions in the modern world.

In 1830, the Blessed Mother appeared to St. Catherine Labouré in Paris, giving her the miraculous medal as a guarantee of her protection. In 1846, she appeared at LaSalette with sober and prophetic words about what would come to pass as one century passed into another. In 1858, St. Bernadette conversed with the "Immaculate Conception" in Lourdes, France. A miraculous, healing spring appeared on the site to confirm the vision. Our Lady appeared in Pontmain, France, in 1871, perhaps to thwart the apostasy in that country that had grown from the seeds of the French Revolution. In Guadalupe, Mexico, Mary appeared as the woman clothed with the sun – in the garb of a woman expecting a baby. In 1917, Our Lady appeared to three children in Fatima, Portugal, promising them that their country would not fall into the hands of a sinister government. That promise has held. At the same time, the Fatima apparitions called all humanity to conversion. She asked for the consecration of Russia to her Immaculate Heart and warned that, if this were not done, that country would spread its errors around the world. As I write, Poland is celebrating the 600th anniversary of the famous icon of Our Lady of Czestochowa.

Our Lady's constant call is to return to prayer. As a physician, I have seen extraordinary things happen as a result of prayer. Now, some of my more scientifically inclined colleagues may find such a statement naïve. These colleagues would do well to read an article published in July 1988 in the *Southern Medical Journal*. In sum, a group of scientists conducted experiments on the therapeutic effects of prayer. The results were astounding.

Lourdes, France, is a familiar spot to traditional Catholics. The name of the place evokes a sense of awe and wonder. Many miracles are associated with Lourdes. The spring that runs there has been a source of physical and emotional healing for many. Over 5000 cures have been documented at Lourdes, and the Church has confirmed sixty-seven miracles after thorough medical and scientific investigation. Lourdes stands as a stunning example of science encountering the power of belief.

No one who travels to Lourdes leaves the same as he or she came. The moral and spiritual healings that take place there are more at times marvelous than the physical cures. Some go to Lourdes armed with a lifetime of prejudices against faith; afterward, skepticism gives way to faith, coldness and antagonism become whole-hearted love of God. As for those who believe, not all of them receive physical healing. They speak, however, of an increase of faith and resignation – true peace of soul.

During the Holy Year of 1983, I was blessed to visit Lourdes with a group of colleagues from the Catholic Physicians Guild of Chicago. Under the auspices of the Blue Army of Our Lady, we did the Alexis Carrel pilgrimage to Rome, Lourdes, and Fatima. After this trip, I no longer felt the need to prove the existence of miracles. I understood that just being alive is miracle enough. God's hand is in all things, natural and supernatural. Life itself is the miracle. I want to share with you what I observed during this trip because I believe that what happens in Lourdes, even in the most ordinary details, bears witness to the connection between faith and healing. I wish that all believing physicians could have this experience.

As the plane touched down, my first impression of France was the tranquility that hung over the landscape. In the middle of the natural beauty of the place lies what was at one time the little village of Lourdes. Today, that village is the largest tourist attraction in France after Paris. It has more hotels than any other city in France, excluding Paris. Modern technology meets and mingles with rural farms and 19th century city structures. Tour busses park next to ancient bridges, buildings, and shrines. Oddly, this strange amalgam works very well, enhancing the charm of the place. During spring and summer months, over two hundred thousand people a day march in procession to the central shrine area surrounding the huge basilica built next to the famous "grotto." This happens twice a day, afternoon and evening.

At the turn of the 19th century, the Vatican established a medical bureau at Lourdes to document reported cures and healings. A long list of such occurrences continues to this day. Every kind of malady has found a cure in Lourdes, crippling and fatal illnesses including tuberculosis and cancer involving almost every organ system of the body. Our pilgrimage group attended a scientific session in the Lourdes medical clinic. We were privileged to hear the medical director's discussions on physical cures at Lourdes. He explained how diligently his office documents the material facts of a case as they are presented including a thorough medical history and physical examination.

Interestingly, often after a healing, a person is reluctant to report it. Many are anxious to return to their own cities to offer thanksgiving to God in their own way without any fanfare. It was often difficult for the medical examiner's office to prevail upon such people to return to the clinic and allow an investigation. Such reluctance was understandable given the time and inconvenience involved. Those who had been healed would have to submit not only to examinations at the time of the cure, but for many years to come since follow-up studies were essential to the process of verification.

As we found our seats in the medical clinic, on ascending tiers for a better view of the discussants, the medical director took out the records of a fairly recent case involving a young Italian woman who had a malignant lesion of the femur. She refused amputation of her leg. The deterioration of the leg continued until she had to be confined to bed. At that point, her family took her by train to Lourdes. They were not seeking a cure, but merely relief of her pain. The year was 1959. After the fistulous tract had been syringed with water from Lourdes' spring, the discharge dried up, the fistula closed, and the bleeding stopped. Almost immediately after her return from Lourdes, the young woman began to gain weight and regain her health. The bone lesion regressed in size. A year later, in 1960, the Medical Bureau met her for the first time. After two more examinations (in 1961 and 1963), this cure was recognized and the file handed to the International Medical Committee. The director ruled "this instantaneous cure, without any convalescence, must be regarded as medically inexplicable." By 1965, the commission declared her cure to be "miraculous."

This narrative reminded me of a talk given years earlier by Father Charles Corcoran, O.P., at the Catholic Physician Guild. The theme of the talk was the difference between the concepts of "curing" and "healing." Today, the distinction between these two notions has become blurred. Emphasis falls on finding cures. As a result, a great deal of research is being done, some for profit, and some supported by charitable donations. There probably exists a charitable foundation for every significant disease in the world. In any case, with such an emphasis in medicine, the most triumphant words a doctor can say to a patient are "you're cured."

Indeed, people can be cured of particular diseases. A cure is for a disease, not a person. This is the difference between curing and healing. One never speaks of healing a disease, only healing a person. A cure is an end, and so is a healing, but in a different way. Healing is a transition from one stage of existence to another. It is often a movement in a life story from one direction to another, the start of something that wasn't there before. A cure, on the other hand, is outwardly applied to outward conditions.

Here is the important part for physicians: A cure may come from the one who heals, but something must also arise from within the one being healed. Patients cannot be healed against their wills.

The conclusion is that healing comes about through the meeting of two people. It is a kind of conversation or dialogue between the two. As in any fruitful discussion, the interlocutors must believe in each other. The one who is sick must believe in the healer, and the healer must believe in the one for whom he or she is caring. Faith is necessary, then, in the healing process even at the human level of patient/physician. A true Catholic physician must be able to restore hope and love in his or her patient so as to enter into inner healing rather than just external care or an external cure.

Father Corcoran also stated that you must not only give your mind in the pursuit of knowledge about God. You must also give your heart so that you love God. As the catechism of my day taught us, our goal is to know, love, and serve God in this world and be happy with him in the next. At the same time, we cannot love God unless we love others who are in the image and likeness of God. The Roman philosopher Tertullian (ca. 160-220), prior to his conversion, exhorted his fellow pagans: "Look at those Christians! Look how they love one another . . . and how they are ready to die for each other."[38]

Many of the professions today, including medicine, are not God centered but man centered. Their philosophy is self-interest. They represent that pagan world to which Tertullian compared the Christians. Paganism believed in many gods who were essentially copies of human characteristics. The gods of paganism did not transcend the human world; they were extreme versions of human beings. The God of Abraham and Moses came onto the scene as something entirely different. The word "holy" comes from an ancient Hebrew word that means "other." God is completely

---

[38] *Apologeticus*, 39.

"other," not just another version of humanity. Jesus Christ brought the otherness of God to earth in the Incarnation. God took on a human face, and human beings received the divine spirit. Christian service means recognizing the face of the Savior in the poor and suffering. It also means possessing the spirit of divine love: charity. There is nothing self-serving or self-centered about the work of a believing physician.

It is a small step from this faith relationship to the greater faith relationship between the soul and God. Jesus is a person. He saves us by healing, not by curing nor by taking our place in living, suffering, dying and rising, but by uniting us to his own Mystical Body so that we share his living, suffering, dying and rising. Moreover, by his death on the cross, Jesus heals the sickness of sin. We must do our own living, suffering, and dying, but the union that we enjoy with Jesus means that our lives are an extension in this world of his life. We contain the possibility of physical healing and physical resurrection because of the union we have with Jesus. Hence, it is possible for miracles to happen. Miracles are a manifestation of Jesus' power as God to save the whole person.

For me, the miracles at Lourdes are proof of the link between faith and healing. Too easily, non-believing physicians disregard Lourdes. If they would take a closer look at the evidence that has been gathered by disinterested members of the scientific community, including members of the medical profession, they would have to surrender the self-centered ideals that motivate them and accept the call of God to a life of charity.

Perhaps Lourdes makes such an impression because it provides the pilgrim with a very tactile experience of faith. The place, the climate, the processions, the prayers and music, the ministering hands and feeling of cold water washing over you – all of this contributes to the sense that in this place heaven and earth meet. I was fortunate to have this experience; its memory gives me a profound sense of peace even to this day. For those who cannot make this journey, here is one pilgrim's version.

After the meetings and lectures with the medical director at the clinic, we joined the throngs of people lining the streets and parks, which lead to the baths of Lourdes. Hundreds of volunteers of all nationalities were milling through the crowds, wearing cloth straps over their shoulders to identify them. They gave completely of themselves to assist people at the baths. Eileen and I and three of our adult children (Maureen, 25; Michelle, 24; and Mary, 20) took our place in the throng. Women were ushered toward one line and men toward another. Directions were plainly marked in German, French, English, and Italian. While we waited (over an hour) we observed other people praying privately or reciting the rosary. We also saw a special line for visitors with special needs: those suffering partial or complete paralysis, cerebral palsy, cancer, hydrocephalus, or the effects of strokes or old age. Family members, children, and volunteers accompanied these special visitors.

After entering through the wrought iron fences leading to the bath doors, the volunteers took in three men at a time. When it was my turn, they walked me to the edge of a brass bathtub filled with two feet of water. They helped me out of my clothes and quietly covered me with a wrap-around towel. The man who assisted me spoke English. It turned out he was from Milwaukee. While helping me into the tub, he told me to pray for a special intention. He then took one arm as another volunteer took the other and submerged me into the water, except for my head. I then kissed the statue of Our Lady, which he held in his hand. This all took only a few seconds. I was amazed at how quickly, efficiently, and reverently everything was done. Even the special needs visitors where handled with the same kind of quiet dispatch.

My body was completely dry as I started to dress. I thanked the volunteers, parted the stiff curtains, and again entered the warm sunlight. Looking into the distance, I felt a deep, inner satisfaction. Perhaps I had shared in the same spirit enjoyed by the followers of St. John the Baptist when he lowered them into the Jordan in a baptism of repentance.

Looking further afield across the park, I could see the hospital with patients lining the balconies. Eileen and the children joined me at the grotto where Mass was being celebrated by Archbishop Nicholas Elko, Msgr. Lorenzetti, and other priests. My son Kevin, a first-year medical student, filmed the Mass on videotape. Later, this recording would help us recall the solemnity of our two days spent in Lourdes.

All meals were served in our hotel. After breakfast, we headed over to the grotto for Mass, prayers, and meditations. Many visitors filled canisters with grotto water to take back home with them. We then headed back to the hotel for lunch and then back to the baths and grotto for the afternoon procession when all in unison said the rosary. After supper, each person purchased a candle in preparation for the evening procession. When darkness fell, the candles were lit and the entire valley became visible. The procession started at the grotto with people twenty to forty across, and then stretched nearly two miles. It was headed first by ambulatory persons followed by visitors in wheelchairs, and then doctors, nurses, and the medical bureau. These were then trailed by as many as 100,000 to 200,000 people. From the top of the basilica, the procession was a majestic sight with everyone praying to God and his mother, doing homage and asking for help for this sinful world. I am certain that astronauts orbiting above could see this line of light stretching over a small part of Southern France.

Though many languages came together in this holy place, silence was the one most heard. Amazingly, 100,000 people could mill through the streets, churches, and the grotto and remain quiet. And on every face, there was a profound expression of tranquility. Truly, we had all stepped out of the familiar world into a preview of heaven. Each day brought more pilgrims by air, train, and car. People came for many reasons, the most frequent one being spiritual healing. I can't help but reflect on the foolishness of people gathering for an event like the Rose Bowl, with all its pageantry, when it means so little. At Lourdes, hundreds of thousands gather to honor the Mother of God, the Mystical Rose, and take away something permanent, something that can heal the soul and the body.

Lourdes proves that faith is alive and well in the world. Despite statistics that the secular media love to throw at us about the loss of religion and the dwindling number of church goers, you have but to spend a few days in Lourdes or the other pilgrimage sites in this world to see that belief in God, his Son, the Blessed Mother, sacraments and prayer is still embraced by great numbers of people. Over the centuries, the Church, under the guidance of the popes, has managed to steer a steady course in regard to its essential beliefs and practices. Although the hierarchy frequently has its problems, it continues to guard a tradition that can trace its origins to the Savior and the apostles he sent out to announce the Good News of salvation. St. Francis Xavier brought the faith to Japan during the Counter-Reformation. St. Paul Miki and his followers maintained it at the cost of martyrdom. Following the dropping of the atomic bomb on Nagasaki, the Catholic history of that city came into view. The Christian faith, once planted, took root.

Following our pilgrimage to Lourdes, the family and I set out for another famous apparition site: Fatima, Portugal. Our tour guide for this part of the trip was Isabella. She was eager for us to discover her country. The Portuguese are a beautiful people, similar in many ways to the Spanish and Italians, yet truly a distinct people. From Lisbon airport, we took a bus into the city on a busy Saturday afternoon. We could sense the unity of this small population of 9 million people.

The hammer and sickle was on all the billboards of the major thoroughfares. According to Isabella, however, the

Portuguese people remained solidly Catholic. The government might have been Communist, but the children still wore their uniforms to school. The family remained the center of Portuguese life, and the Catholic faith remained deeply interwoven with all aspects of social, economic, and educational activity. History proves that Communism succeeds only where faith is weak and the men of the Church have become corrupt. When faith is strong and the hierarchy is faithful, as in Italy, Poland, Spain, and Portugal, Communism cannot get a deep hold on the culture. Of all countries of Europe, Portugal proves this point more than any other.

The family, I feel, is central to the defeat of totalitarian systems like Communism. It has been said that the family is the strongest philosophy because it spans five generations – at least one hundred years – and consequently no anti-family philosophy has ever been successful for very long. Communism, socialism, humanism, materialism, and other such ideologies come and go while family endures. In our own time, the socialist agenda evident in gay activism and the push for an Equal Rights Amendment illustrates an anti-family philosophy that has been with humanity from the biblical days of Sodom and Gomorrah through the homosexual culture of the ancient Greeks, right up to the debates in our legislatures about gay marriage.

As the bus left meandered through small towns on the way to Fatima, we could see neat, little farms eking out a living from the soil. Archbishop Elko took this time to tell us the story of the "miracle of Santarem." Apparently, in the 16th century, a young Portuguese girl from Santarem sought out a fortuneteller in order to obtain a favor. The fortuneteller promised to fulfill her request if she brought to her a consecrated host. The young lady went to Mass shortly after and received Holy Communion. Instead of consuming the host, however, she removed it from her mouth, wrapped it in her dress, and took it home. On her way, blood began to drip from the dress. She became frightened and hid the host in a chest. She could not keep the secret long, however. When her husband discovered what she had done, he made her return the host to the church. It had turned a bright red color, like a blood clot. The priest placed the bloody host in a monstrance (a receptacle that allows a host to be seen).

The story of the "miracle of Santarem" is painted on the walls of the village church. Faith, like patriotism, to remain strong requires stories that vividly recreate original experiences and heroic deeds so that a society remains rooted in the reasons for its beliefs and practices. Every Portuguese child who visits the church of Santarem has a visible account of a great miracle; every adult, in seeing those walls, is reminded of true Portuguese identity. To destroy a cultural identity or a religion all that is necessary is the de-emphasis, distortion, or complete effacement of such stories. The destruction of customs, the eroding of heritage, the disappearance of feast days and memorial occasions little by little saps the soul of a people, re-writing their history in order to give rise to a change in belief and customs. In Portugal, however, the story of the miracle of Santarem endures and, along with it, an abiding sense of Catholic identity. It has been suggested by many that the miracle of Santarem, more than the apparitions at Fatima, was responsible for the strong faith of the Portuguese. It explains also the strong faith of Columbus and Queen Isabella, as well as King Peter of Brazil and the world explorers Vasco de Gama and Magellan. Faith accompanied the Portuguese everywhere they explored and established colonies. Thanks to the Portuguese, a great part of the world heard the Gospel message and the Catholic faith took root among many native peoples.

Arriving in Santarem, we could see the medieval design of the town. The bus could not pass through its narrow, winding streets. We alighted at a coffee shop and made our way past many storefront and homes to a narrow but impressive three-story church with its bell tower and old, double-entrance doors leading respectively to the left and right side aisles of the church. Posters on the doors announced coming feast day activities. Inside the church, we found simple, wooden kneelers and pews. We said the rosary as a group and then Archbishop Elko and Msgr. Lorenzetti brought out the monstrance containing the famous bleeding host of Santarem for us to view.

Having had a little taste of Portuguese religious tradition, we were now eager to visit Fatima. We had grown up hearing about the events in that little village. Who could forget the stories about the three children who had seen and spoken with the Blessed Mother? And what of the "miracle of the Sun," that great event witnessed by thousands that proved the truth of what the children related? We were now to set foot on the very spot about which we had heard over the course of a lifetime. I remembered the class I had as a child.

In the middle of my recollections, the bus pulled up to the hotel. We filed inside and ate a late afternoon snack provided by the hotel. We were then assigned to three floors of very neat rooms. Everyone was eager to explore the areas that in 1919 suddenly received international attention. We rose early the next morning and walked to the shrine a few blocks north. Already, people were gathering. We went to a recently dedicated, large stone edifice that was only partially enclosed. The government, for the arrival the previous year of Pope John Paul II, had built it. Here he had met Sr. Lucia, the sole surviving visionary of Fatima. Jacinta and Francesco died not long after the apparitions ended.

Archbishop Elko said Mass for all the pilgrims and related how fortunate we were to again visit a site where the Mother of God had bestowed her blessings. Every mystery of the Catholic Church, from the days of the apostles until now, fits into divine logic. If people could cease worrying about tomorrow and place their entire confidence in God, they would find immediate peace and security. The three children of Fatima, like Bernadette of Lourdes, accepted the visions and did not for a moment question Our Lady's wishes. The bishop, priests, and local government officials all questioned the verity of the children's story, even to the extent of placing these little ones in jail. Doing so only served to spread the messages of Fatima.

The Archbishop went on to describe divine logic and action in the history of the Church. God gave us the Bible, the

Church, and the saints. Since the death of the apostles, our history has been full of extraordinary events that guide us through times of world crisis. Great men and women of the Church have transcended their times with heroic action. Sometimes, it takes years for the truth to come out. St. Joan of Arc's executioners did not allow her to kiss a makeshift cross as she burned at the stake. A decade later, the French people declared her a saint. Her case was eventually reopened, and her conviction overturned. She remains to this day a great symbol of personal integrity. Reversals of a narrative happen when history reveals the full truth. Forty years after his death, the world can finally acknowledge the wisdom and courage of Pope Pius XII to remain neutral in World War II in order to save countless Jews.

With pious devotion, we pilgrims hastened to the site were the Blessed Mother appeared to the three children. At the town of Cova, just a few miles south, we stopped on a rugged terrain dotted with cork trees and olive trees. We prayed the Stations of the Cross and then the rosary, led by a Canadian hospital orderly and his French wife (who spoke no English). S. M. Couer of Pennsylvania refreshed us on the history of the apparitions that occurred from March to September 1919. We stopped approximately one mile from the apparition site at a corner dress shop and coffee store to buy some post cards. When we heard that the cousin of Jacinta and Joaquin, was present, we hurried to his house to have our pictures taken with him. He appeared to be in his seventies and was dressed very simply. He lived in a small, two-room wooden house just down the dirt road street where Lucia was born. Joaquin refused, so the story goes, to tell Jacinta and Francisco that Lucia had seen the Virgin Mary until she gave him a coin, a Pasita.

We were then taken to the International Shrine of the Blue Army of Our Lady. This shrine exists to obtain peace in the world by enrolling enough people to outnumber Communist party members. It contains an Eastern Byzantine Church constructed in honor of Our Lord and His Mother. The famous "Icon of Kazan" is safely housed here. Tradition tells us that the icon belong to the Russian Orthodox Church. In 1919, about the same time as the Fatima apparitions, the icon was stolen from the Russian Church in Moscow by the local community part in order to raise money for their revolution. It somehow ended up in England where it was purchased by a wealthy Englishman. About ten years prior to our visit, the icon was put up for auction. Though the exiled Russian hierarchy in the United States wish to purchase the sacred relic, they lacked the funds. By chance, the Blue Army acquired it, and it now resides in Fatima. Once Russia is converted again to Christianity, it will be returned to the Russian Orthodox Church. Dating back to the Middle Ages, the Icon of Kazan depicts the Blessed Mother. It is approximately four by three feet and is adorned with golf leaf and jewels. After our visit, the curtain was closed again on this beautiful relic.

Not all of our time in Portugal was directly related to the faith. We had a splendid evening celebrating the Age of Chivalry at a medieval banquet. Our group filled up two tour buses that carried us to the bottom of a hill. The sun was just setting when we heard trumpets sounding from the top of the hill. To our surprise, a medieval castor of a fortress projected out above us. We could see a man on a white horse. He came down the hillside and informed us that we were all invited to the castle for dinner. Taxis stood nearby to transport us up the hill to the recently renovated castle. We were later informed that an American and his wife had been conducting these banquets nightly for the past ten years; grateful for the favors they had received from Our Lady of Fatima. They gave up their residences in the United States and devoted all of their energies to this pursuit.

Upon arrival, a few of us were assigned special titles, given crowns, and led to the head table. Archbishop Elka was designated King Peter, and Sister M. Couer became Queen Isabella. We were entertained with a skit concerning the religious hierarchy of Portugal through the turbulent Middle Ages. I sat next to Sister M. Couer during dinner. After the play, one of the actresses handed a long-stem rose to her as a parting gesture to the "queen." Sister began to cry. I didn't know what to make of the situation. It seemed out of keeping with what had happened. Later, however, Sister explained to me that over the past year she had been praying to Our Blessed Mother for a special favor. She asked that, if she were to receive this favor, the sign would be the gift of a long-stem rose. Many times she had been in places where there were roses, but no one had offered her a rose until this night. All I could think was that sister's gift was a fitting climax to our pilgrimage. In some way, we all had received a rose during this special time of grace. We returned to the United States the next day.

In this chapter, I have sought to share with my readers the experiences of an integrated Christian life. We are body and soul. Our faith is a theological gift that is meant to manifest itself in time and space. We are surrounded by what St. Paul described as "a cloud of witnesses." We have places like Lourdes and Fatima, the Shroud of Turin, the Dead Sea scrolls, the bones of St. Peter discovered under the main altar of St Peter's in Rome, the bodies of incorruptible saints in all corners of the globe – and so much more. Such things support and nourish our faith. They help us believe even when there is no physical evidence. At the same time, faith gives us a special vision denied to those who do not believe. In the words of the great medieval theologian St. Thomas Aquinas, "For those with faith, no explanation is necessary. For those without faith, no explanation is possible.

Chapter Ten

Suffering and Sacrifice

*Unless we recover the zeal and the spirit of the
first century Christians – unless we are willing
to do what they did and to pay the price that
they paid, the future of our country, the days of
America are numbered. – Fr. Hardon*

There is a close relationship between medicine and
religion that has been recognized since ancient times.
Christianity, however, is the only faith that offers a consistent
explanation of this relationship. It explains why there is
sickness and death in the world and why there exists a medical
profession. For some, the explanation of all human suffering
is sin; the motivation for all healing professions is charity.

For the Christian, suffering is charged with meaning.
It exists to make people conscious of their need for God. It
detaches them from the desire for things of this world and
increases in them a desire for God and the spiritual gifts that
come from God. Finally, God permits suffering as a means of
sanctification and purification in this life so that human beings
may attain the joy of the Beatific Vision in the world to come.
Hence, suffering for suffering's sake has no place in the

Christian schema. To think that it does is heretical. Suffering is good only when it serves the plan of God and is accepted as such, freely and with the spirit of charity.

In this chapter, I would like to comment on the strange distortion that has entered into the popular mind about suffering and sacrifice. True sacrifice, the heroic road to holiness, has been re-defined as an expression of an individual's personal desires and ego fulfillment. The results are devastating for our culture, particularly for the young who by nature seek the adventure of high ideals. What kind of heroes are we giving them to imitate today? As a physician, I have seen many kinds of suffering; physical suffering, of course, but also mental and spiritual suffering. I have seen people who struggled in anguish against disease and death. I have also known people who enjoyed profound inner peace in the midst of chronic or deteriorating illness.

The trajectory of pain for a patient is very interesting. Acute episodes require analgesic medication (pain killers). The rupture of a viscus, pancreatitis, lung tumors, perforation of a stomach ulcer, appendicitis – all of these events and so many more cause excruciating pain. An occlusion of the small coronary arteries requires immediate relief of pain or it may turn fatal. In some cases, however, pain medication is not necessarily required. Pain centers in the brain can become desensitized; nerves can deteriorate. Either way, I have noticed that in both cases – a stable plateau or continuing deterioration – some patients are able to bear their condition without pain medication. This tells us something about how human beings suffer. Acceptance of pain is half the equation;

turning that pain into something meaningful is the other half of the equation.

As I prepare the final version of this book, the media is focusing everyone's attention on former Gold-medal Olympian Bruce Jenner. Vanity Fair has just published an article about his assumed identity as "Caitlyn Jenner." The response from most quarters has been to hail Jenner's courage and personal sacrifice for being his "true" self. Just a few years ago, "coming out" as a homosexual person was praised as an act of heroism. Now, focus has shifted to being transgender. What will be next? Will we see the label "heroic" on those who admit that they are in polygamous marital relationships? Will we see it used to describe adults sexually exploiting children? Will the admission of bestiality merit praise? The slippery slope argument has proven itself to be valid, and present evils may be tomorrow's goods.

Without a doubt, our culture has lost the true meaning of sacrifice. The individual has become his or her own ultimate good. The measure of heroism, therefore, is how much you are willing to bear not for another, but for yourself. To sacrifice is to seek that to which you are entitled, even at the cost of injury to another person, a family, or a community. You are heroic when you "stand up for yourself" or "speak your truth" or "realize yourself." What an ego-centric world we have become!

I come from another generation that defined heroism quite differently. Heroism meant standing up for the truth, yes, but not merely a subjective, personal truth. Real heroism meant standing up for an objective truth, that is, a good *outside* of yourself. Moreover, sacrifice did not refer only to what you might suffer. It had a greater reach. Sacrifice entailed suffering because it recognized the "sacredness" of something or someone. In sacrificing for your children, for example, you recognized them as a good worthy of your self-donation. In serving your country, you recognized the good of the values that define your people's way of life. In sacrificing for God, you recognized the ultimate Good to whom you owed everything. What passes for sacrifice now pales in comparison to these heroic, self-transcending ideals.

Sacrifice used to be a virtue, an act to respect and emulate. People who made great sacrifices were the real heroes of the world. They lived through their heroic ordeals. We honored them. Living through the World War II era, my generation had many such heroes. The press and the news reels that preceded every movie brought us stories of brave and men and women at home and abroad who gave their all to resist tyranny and help those who could not help themselves. The movies, too, kept before us the idea that human greatness had something to do with truth, courage, and self-transcendence.

Since World War II, we have inverted the natural order of human self-realization. Instead of citizens seeking the good of all, we are a nation of individuals out for their own personal gain. Once in a while, a bright light shines to remind us who we once were. John F. Kennedy was such a light throughout his presidency. The words of his 1960 inaugural address inspired a nation: "Think not of what your country can do for you, but what you can do for your country." Kennedy offered young people a vision of a future that they could shape by their generosity and self-donation. He established the Peace Corps to give Americans a chance to share the blessings of education and practical know-how with struggling peoples. Many youth answered Kennedy's call to work in foreign lands. Others bent their energies to the task of improving things at home or achieving great technological and scientific advances, such as putting a man on the moon. For a brief time, Americans felt the pride that accompanies self-sacrifice and a common effort to realize the good of all.

The end of the Kennedy presidency marked the end of an era of optimism. The assassinations of Robert Kennedy and Martin Luther King, Jr., along with the escalating situation in Vietnam sent the country on a downward spiral.

But the notion of sacrifice, I feel, has not completely disappeared from this world. In the sixties and seventies, while convents and seminaries were closing all over the United States, Mother Theresa was busy opening new centers to serve "the poorest of the poor" all over the world. She even did so in the major cities of North and South America. The only qualifications necessary to join her congregation were the ability to work and pray, and the willingness to take vows of poverty, chastity, and obedience. Mother Theresa asked for a life of total sacrifice from her people, and she got it.

In my years as a physician, I had many opportunities to witness true heroism. I saw extraordinary self-sacrifice not only from caretakers, but also in the way many patients accepted infirmity and death. In some cases, my colleagues and I had only a hint of the magnitude of a soul's self-offering.

In heaven, we will understand fully what we have only seen in part.

One case that has stayed with me over the years was that of Virginia Reske, a twenty-five year old woman who fell off a horse. For three years, she remained in a coma on a medical floor of St. Francis Hospital. The Franciscan sisters and the nursing staff took immaculate care of her. Each day, I would pass by her room on my rounds. She was usually sitting up in a wheelchair. Her legs and arms made only purposeless movements. Though she appeared alert, she couldn't speak or focus her eyes. She had to be fed through a tube. It was impossible to say how much Virginia was aware of her surroundings. Did she understand what was going on around her? Was she in "locked brain syndrome" insofar as she could understand but could not communicate? Some in the medical profession might say she was in a "vegetative state."

Virginia lived in this condition for fourteen years at St. Francis Hospital before finally succumbing to pneumonia. Today, it might be argued that Virginia had no "real" life; it might be suggested that she should have been allowed to die by starvation – or helped along by "assisted" suicide. I am not an ethicist, but I am certain that such thinking is fundamentally flawed. My certitude rests not on the teaching of the Church (which is entirely correct in these matters), but on the experience of working as a physician with Virginia and many others in her condition. The truth is that the good gained by many witnessing Virginia was inestimable. We will not understand it fully until we reach the other side. Both she and her family set an example of Christian faith, hope, and love.

Virginia's mother founded a volunteer organization at St. Francis Hospital that eventually spread to other neighboring hospitals. These groups called itself "candy stripers" and were identifiable by their red and white striped uniforms. The candy stripers were high school students who helped to feed and assist patients, especially those with greater needs. Virginia's caretakers also shone with the light of charity; people like Sister Frances Xavier who spent many a day ministering to Virginia's special needs.

And what about the daily lessons in wisdom that people like Virginia teach simply by existing? They remind us – nurses, doctors, and other patients – that we are alive to serve through stewardship. None of us can lift a finger without the grace of God, nor is there anything we possess – life, health, goods – that does not come from the hand of God. Our task in this life is to accept with gratitude and humility God's gifts and honor Him by caring for them. This is what it means to be a "steward." At the moment of death, Christ will demand an accounting of our stewardship.

Our culture no longer recognizes the gift of someone like Virginia or the meaningfulness of her life. We have lost sight of the greater human goods, namely, the spiritual goods that people like Virginia can call forth in others. While no one would willingly take on such a cross or wish it on another, this is not to say that it is without value. Christ worked daily through Virginia for fourteen years. Only in heaven will there be a true accounting of all the good she did, but we can say for now that her witness was two-fold: She gave us all a reason to appreciate and thank God for the gift of health. She also gave us an opportunity to serve someone less fortunate than ourselves and to do so without complaining. She stirred compassion in us. She helped us to not take our good health for granted.

It is my belief that people like Virginia cultivate in us moral and spiritual goods that transcend any good of this world, including health. The current discussion over assisted suicide does consider these goods. We are on yet another slippery slope. Without an appreciation for goods that come from human suffering, efforts to eliminate suffering will have no bounds. The goal of life will not be heroic witness, but escape.

The current media celebration of Bruce Jenner's "heroism," is indicative of a loss of sense about the true meaning of sacrifice. But let us assume for a moment that there really is such a thing as gender dysphoria. Let us assume that Bruce Jenner suffered for many years with the conviction that he was in the wrong body. What answer could be given to him? What answer could we give many other people who suffer and have chosen to end the suffering by altering nature or choosing to end life before its natural end?

Here is our answer: sacrifice. Sacrifice is not suffering. It is a universe apart! Sacrifice comes from two Latin words: "sacra," meaning, "holy," and "fare," meaning, "to do or make." In other words, sacrifice means "to make something holy." Too often, the word is associated with deprivation or self-inflicted discomfort. In reality, a sacrifice elevates the thing sacrificed, making it worthy before God. God is the definition of "holy," a word that translates from the ancient

Hebrew meaning "completely other." When we sacrifice something, we lift it up to God so that it can become a channel of his redemptive power. Divine grace enters the world through sacrifice because Jesus made the cross the means of salvation. Every human being who accepts suffering as sacrifice shares in the suffering of Christ and, as a result, becomes a co-participant in redemption. St. Paul said as much: "Now I rejoice in what I am suffering for you, and I fill up in my flesh what is still lacking in regard to Christ's afflictions, for the sake of his body, which is the church" (Col. 1:24).

As a physician, I have seen a great deal of human suffering. Suffering is a fact of human existence, as inevitable as death. While it is right and just that we work for the alleviation of suffering, we must do so in accord with nature and the higher spiritual values that define us as human beings. We must act with the knowledge that every choice we make for ourselves is a choice for all people. We set principles by opting for some actions over others. When Bruce Jenner "comes out," when Brittany Maynard has her life ended by assisted suicide, when a woman chooses to abort her child – all such actions send a message to the world that suffering must be avoided at all costs.

But the situation is worse than that. To put it in simple terms, our society is exalting cowardice and calling it courage. "Heroism" has been redefined as the avoidance of suffering, not the courage of facing and overcoming it. In fact, people who practice true heroism, that is, who suffer in the name of truth and justice, receive scarce attention if not scorn. Ask any person today to name "heroes" they have seen on television or the movies. The list will be long. Ask them to name people who have or are truly sacrificing themselves for the common good, and how many names will you hear? The fault, of course, lies with a media that seeks the titillating and perverse – such as the Jenner story – in order to keep the public enthralled and coming back for more.

It's odd that we live in a time when superheroes are so popular, yet genuine heroism is not. The goal of life has become the creation of a pain-free world where everyone can live complacent and worry-free. In addition to the impossibility of this utopic notion, human psychology is not constructed to do well without purpose or challenge. Let us be cautious about our choice of challenges. We can challenge ourselves to realize a personal agenda, or we can submit ourselves to the trial of accomplishing a task greater than us. A person can accept physical suffering and not opt for assisted suicide because of a desire to bear witness to the sacredness of life. A person can live a chaste life, even if struggling with same sex attraction or transgender, in order to bear witness to the true meaning of sexuality in the marital union of man and woman. A person can accept an inconvenient or crisis pregnancy as a testament to the value of every human life. In all such cases, sacrifice and the essential goods that define it, transform suffering, and are not merely affirmed, but nourished. People who make such sacrifices become beacons of light and hope; they are true paradigms of human dignity.

How sorely we are in need of such people today!

Chapter Eleven

Prescription for Health: Spiritual Jogging

*I have fought the good fight. I have finished
the race. I have kept the faith.*
St. Paul (2 Timothy 4:7)

A healthy person must be well in body and soul. This is so because body and soul are so intimately joined that the health of one inevitably influences the health of the other.

Another point is important. The reciprocal relationship of body and soul does not mean that the two are equal. In fact, the soul has priority over the body because it is the source of the body's life and functions. The physical movement of the body is only the surface appearance of unseen movements in the soul. Life originates and is maintained by the soul; hence, spirit has priority over flesh. What this means is that in balancing body and soul, the human being must work from the inside out. Health is first and foremost an inside job.

Over the years, I have developed a way of looking at spiritual health that parallels physical health. Drawing on my knowledge as a physician of what happens when the body exercises, I have come up with a schema for building up the health of the soul. In sum, physical jogging can serve as an analogy for what I call "spiritual jogging."

Let's start with the body. Physical exercise produces chemical substances called "endorphins." Endorphins are natural pain killers. They also produce a natural state of euphoria. People who jog regularly call the feeling they get "runner's high." The description is a good one since joggers can become addicted to this special feeling. They will say that without their daily jog, they don't feel right. Such die-hards run in all weather conditions no matter what else is happening in their lives.

In addition to feeling good, many joggers experience deep inner peace when they run. They have moments of insight about what to do in certain practical matters in their lives. While the body exerts itself, the mind is open and free to soar, fueled by the positive impulses of endorphins and an increase in oxygen.

Much of what I have just described can be found in an analogous way in what I call "spiritual jogging." Just as physical jogging produces a natural state of bliss, spiritual jogging fills the soul with supernatural joy. Prayer, in fact, elevates the soul, placing it in the presence of God – the ultimate endorphin.

I would love to claim originality, but I'm afraid St. Paul was way ahead of me on this one. Many times in his letters, he compares the Christian life, not to mention his own apostolic activity, to the determination of an athlete running a race. In the *Acts of the Apostles*, for example, he is quoted as saying, "I consider my life worth nothing to me, if only I may finish the race and complete the task the Lord Jesus has given me—the task of testifying to the gospel of God's grace" (Acts 20:24). Some years later, reflecting on his approaching martyrdom, he writes, "I have fought the good fight, I have finished the race, I have kept the faith" (2 Timothy 4:7).

St. Paul captures the discipline and determination of the serious jogger. In fact, spiritual joggers can learn something from their physical counterparts. Joggers aim at being as physically fit as possible. They will train for months to improve their strength and endurance. Often, their daily jog is preparation for a big race, maybe even a marathon. Joggers are willing to sacrifice a lot to achieve an optimum state of health. They will give up time and social activities. They will eat healthy foods and get up at early hours.

Similarly, those who are bent on attaining spiritual health make sacrifices. Writing to the Christian community at Corinth, St. Paul states: "Do you not know that in a race all the runners run, but only one gets the prize? Run in such a way as to get the prize. Everyone who competes in the games goes into strict training. They do it to get a crown that will not last; but we do it to get a crown that will last forever" (1 Corinthians 9:24-25). The author of the Letter to the Hebrews has this to say: "Lay aside every weight, and the sin which so easily ensnares us, and let us run with endurance the race that is set before us, looking unto Jesus, the author and finisher of our faith" (Hebrews 12:1-2).

People engaged in spiritual jogging avoid everything that might make the soul sluggish or heavy. Material wealth is a danger over which they must be very vigilant. The more human beings grasp at things, the less they have hold of themselves. Body and soul suffer from the undue pursuit of wealth, as I can well attest from my experience as a physician. Emotional ills top the list of diseases common to our more affluent citizens. Many of these people have more need of a psychiatrist than a family physician.

Speaking as a physician, I have noticed that people who enjoy spiritual health tend to have better physical and psychological health. Although doctors care for the body, it is impossible to be so engaged without noticing the state of the soul. As I said earlier, body and soul are connected; the one impacts the other. Spiritual unrest can be at the root of problems like depression, anxiety, obesity, hypertension, and peptic ulcer. Spiritual ill-health can lead to addictions to alcohol, drugs, and sex.

The word "health" is a general term implying "at ease." The opposite of health, of course, is "disease" or "dis-ease," that is, "ill at ease." A soul that is ill at ease with itself is ripe for physical illness. The spiritual aspect of the human being includes the ability of reason. A long-standing tradition has maintained three essential aspects of the human being: intellect, will, and desire. Human beings don't just do things. They *know* that they are doing things; they are aware of the inner processes and desires that bring them to do things.

Moreover, human beings know that certain actions are appropriate, while others are not. This aspect of reason is called "conscience," a word that means "with knowledge." Moved by desire, the human being uses reason to discern good from evil, and then exercises the will in one direction or another. The person who chooses to do evil is "ill at ease" because an evil action violates what that person's conscience knows to be true. The Ten Commandments are written on the heart. They are, so to speak, instinctive inclinations for human beings. Just as the body inclines towards foods containing essential nutrients, so does the soul incline toward thoughts and actions that nourish it.

Adults may be able to cover up this inner drama. Children cannot. When children lie to their parents, they are immediately ill at ease, and the indications are very evident: eyes shifting, face blushing, head down, voice raised or rushing. A parent does not need a degree in psychology to understand what is happening. As soon as the lie is admitted and forgiven, order is restored and the physical signs of disorder vanish. If children are not corrected when they lie, they may acquire the habit of lying. Constant suppression of conscience eventually produces a desensitized soul and an impenetrable façade. The result is a disharmony between soul and body.

Spiritual jogging, then, is a discipline that should begin early. Parents and guardians should help children elevate their souls through awareness of what is good and just. This means orienting them toward healthy relationships with family, neighbors, school friends and, most importantly, themselves. Self-esteem grows to the measure that children value themselves as good and worthy of love. Children are naturally spiritual; they respond eagerly to religious direction. Honoring God and showing respect for human beings, including themselves, leads to life-long spiritual health.

I don't mean to imply that spiritual jogging is easy. Physical jogging, once it becomes a habit, may be enjoyable, but it will always require the discipline of hauling oneself out of bed early in the morning. To become physically strong, we have to submit the body to pain and effort. In the same way, spiritual jogging requires discipline and, at times, discomfort. Why is this so? Ask Adam and Eve!

The *Book of Genesis* in the bible tells us that in the beginning human beings were in a perfect state of physical and spiritual health and happiness. After they disobeyed God's commandment not to eat of the Tree of Life, their physical and spiritual powers, though still good, fell into disorder. The priority of the spirit over the flesh was lost; henceforth, it would be a battle between spirit and flesh. The body would weigh down the soul with its demands for natural satisfactions. The soul would have to be constantly vigilant to reign in the body, allowing it what was right and healthy and steering it clear from what was wrong and unhealthy.

Although we tend to see Adam and Eve as solely responsible for death and suffering, the truth is, there was another being at work in Eden the day our first parents ate of the Tree of Life. Scripture indicates that a battle had taken place in heaven. The angel Lucifer rebelled against God. He and legions of followers fought St. Michael the Archangel and the hosts of heaven. Satan's forces were defeated, a third of them being cast down to earth. I remember the impression that this story made upon me as a young boy. In those days, every Mass ended with the priest reciting prayers that recalled the battle between the principalities and the powers: "St. Michael the Archangel, defend us in battle. Be our safeguard against the wickedness and snares of the devil. Do though, O Prince of the Heavenly Host, by the power of God, cast into hell Satan and all the other evils spirits who prowl about the world, seeking the ruin of souls." According to Scripture and tradition, hell lies at the core of the earth. While speaking with Pilate, Our Lord said that his kingdom is not of this world. In fact, we live in enemy territory, and our lives are passed in a battle between the forces of evil and the power of Divine Grace.

Original sin, then, is the true cause of the ills that plague us. Through the centuries, both soul and body have been co-involved in the battle against disease and death. Despite the astounding progress of medical science in recent times, human beings still fall ill; they still die. Even today, few people live past forty thousand days. The medieval mystic and writer Thomas a Kempis reminds us to pray before bedtime as if we were not to see the dawn. We should ask our guardian angel to guide us in the night to our heavenly reward. In the same way, if we awaken, we should greet the new day with the awareness that we may not see its sunset. The point is to be prepared, whether sleeping or waking, for the final account we must give of our lives. Living in this way, we shall have health of soul and body. We will enjoy inner peace.

On the subject of guardian angels, we could say that these spiritual friends are our "soul trainers." Sacred Scripture and long-standing tradition acknowledge that God has assigned to each person a special spiritual helper – an angel to watch over body and soul. Guardian angels whisper to our souls. They advise, caution, encourage, and incline us away from what is harmful and toward what is good. Saint Pio of Pietrolina, better known as "Padre Pio," was a Capuchin monk and stigmatic who lived in Italy. Guardian angels visited him in his rooms at night to discuss the problems they were having with their wards. While hearing confessions, Padre Pio would advise his penitents not to make a return trip to Italy to see him, but send their guardian angels instead!

As a physician, I can bear witness to the never-ending battle between health and disease. Even now, at the beginning of the 21st century, we continue to discover new and more complex diseases, such as immune deficiency syndromes or environmental and occupational disorders. We have developed amazing ways of treating disease: surgery with laser beams, organ transplants, and cryosurgery. We can even "grow" organs now from stem cells. Sometimes, it seems that medical science will one day place immortality within reach of humanity.

Though scientists continue to unravel the mysteries of creation, they have yet to come up with a plan to change the human heart. In order for human well-being to be fully achieved, I believe human beings must change. They must accept the order that God has given the universe. They must obey the demands of this order. Only then will individuals experience unity of body and soul. Only then will our society manifest the harmony of members at peace with themselves.

My "prescription," if you will, is daily spiritual jogging. How does one jog spiritually? Daily prayer is the most perfect way to enter the race. Prayer is always possible, no matter where you are or what you are doing. Prayer is defined simply as "the lifting of the heart and mind to God." It does not require any special place or words or props. I used to take advantage of my daily commute back and forth from home to the hospital or office to talk to God. In these moments, I confided to God my worries. I discussed with him the details of my everyday life, as well as my big concerns. The act of praying reaps reward for mind and body. It quiets the nerves and releases tension. Praying is good for you!

In some instances, spiritual health becomes the means by which people can endure disabling physical illness. Over the years, I have seen many incapacitated bodies, some in emergency rooms and others in public places like beaches and airports. I have seen them even in far-flung areas such as Mexico, Brazil, and the jungles of Africa.

The most unique case I ever had was that of a young lady of twenty-six years who became a patient of mine. Her family called to ask if I would examine their daughter for an upper respiratory infection. They explained to me that she had been an invalid since birth and that her mother and sister would bring her to my office.

The day she came, we were extremely busy. All our examining rooms were filled. For my part, I had completely forgotten about the phone call. Hence, when I opened the door to the examining room, I was unprepared for what I found. The patient was sitting on the examination table. Her head was of normal proportions, but her body was very small – perhaps three feet at the most. Her torso, in fact, seemed to constitute the whole person. Here was someone who had never walked and had to be carried everywhere. Her body, arms, and legs had not developed since the age of one. Poliomyelitis, often called simply "polio" or infantile paralysis, was the obvious diagnosis. The disease had involved the lower cervical area of the spinal cord, allowing her to breathe with her abdominal muscles only.

Accompanying the young woman was her mother and sister. I felt the love of the little group as soon as I opened the door. The patient, however, was extremely ill. She was short of breath, and her temperature was quite high. Her face was flush, and a hacking cough broke up her greeting to me. Even so, she immediately put me at ease with her gracious smile. Her face and countenance were beautiful; her personal hygiene immaculate. This was a beautiful soul entrusted to a body that depended on spiritual jogging for health. For twenty-six years she had given love and joy to her parents, siblings, and neighbors. They reciprocated those sentiments. An examination revealed that pneumonia was present in her lungs. Antibiotics were prescribed. In the early 1960s, for persons of her size, respirators and blood gas machines to monitor breathing parameters were unavailable. The prognosis could go either way. She could improve on her own as she had done in the past, or lapse into a coma, unable to remove carbon dioxide from her lungs.

This beautiful soul, temporarily imprisoned in her own body, was nonetheless in better health than most human beings because she was at peace. For twenty-six years she jogged spiritually by thanking God daily for what he had given her. Her prayer was not that of complaint, but of blessing. We would say today that she had an "attitude of gratitude." Her daily exercise of faith and blessing, her spiritual jogging, made her a robust, healthy soul that could fill a room with joy.

Spiritual jogging moves us first toward God and then toward neighbor. Few people are called to the life of a hermit. Most of us will spend our time on earth involved with people. Speaking as a physician, I have noticed that the greater part of individual health problems in the United States are directly related to interpersonal relationships. These relationships face many challenges: differences of language, value systems, cultural practices and ideals, and economic status, just to name a few. We now enjoy instant communication with almost every corner of the earth, yet we remain as a species at odds over so many issues. Our technology is ahead of our capacity to relate to one another.

We can adapt to our new world situation. The human being is amazingly adaptable. Consider this example of the body's adaptability. Many millennia ago, when human beings arrived in Africa, they were confronted with malarial plagues. Over time, the blood of Africans adapted to deal with the pathogen causing malaria. While some today continue to maintain a 90% biconcave blood cell shape, others have blood cells that are 60% biconcave and 40% sickle shaped. The malaria parasite cannot reside in individuals with sickle shaped blood cells.

Adaptability is possible at the spiritual level, too. In this case, what we are talking about is adaptation to the Laws of God. Spiritual jogging requires that are interpersonal relationships be ruled by the Ten Commandments. The first three of the commandments describe how we must relate to God our Creator. We must worship only God, keep the Sabbath, and never take God's name in vain. The other commandments refer to human beings. They address our relationship with our parents ("Honor your father and your mother") and then other people, both friends and enemies. The Ten Commandments are a blue print for a happy, healthy human community. The spiritual jogger sees them as the ultimate training program. Our world today could use the guidance of the Ten Commandments. Government agencies and international efforts to improve the human condition often fail in their efforts because their aims oppose the Laws of God. The United Nations and its agency the World Health Organization seek the good of human beings without acknowledging God or his commandments. They are destined to fail and compound the errors of their secular materialistic foundations. Once the United Nations assembly accepts God as the Creator and pays homage to Him, once the World Health Organization accepts Divine rule and orders its goals and efforts according to natural law, then and only then will "health" have genuine meaning. Then and only then will it become an attainable goal.

I'm often reminded of my surgical professor at Cook County Hospital who believed in strict discipline and order. "How could a human being do justice to his patients as a surgeon if first his own house isn't in order?" If our habits as physicians were slovenly and our speech and manner inappropriate, how could we be healers of others? I think my professor would appreciate my plan for spiritual jogging. In essence, I am suggesting that we embrace a daily discipline of putting our house in order. Prayer is the source, a mind informed by divine and natural law is the guide, and a will bent on the practice of justice and cultivation of the virtues is the means.

Just how healthy can spiritual jogging make you? Well, it could make you healthy enough to live on nothing but a consecrated host. It might even keep your body from decomposing after death. These two miracles, called respectively "inedia" and "incorruptibility," have been well recorded in history and bear witness to the body/soul connection I have been describing. The phenomenon of inedia is voluntary abstinence from food and drink. It is not self-starvation. Recently, a Taliban terrorist died after sixty-five days of abstinence from food and drink. This was self-immolation, not inedia. Inedia must also be distinguished from anorexia nervosa, a mental disorder confined almost exclusively to women. Anorexia does not appear in times of famine, but rather, afflicts affluent women in wealthy countries. Finally, inedia is not the result of illness or the infestation of tape worms. Properly understood, inedia is "holy fasting" that allows only for the daily consumption of the consecrated host which is, materially speaking, unleavened bread (it contains no yeast) made from wheat flour. According to Holy Scripture, both Moses and Christ both went for forty days without food.

In modern times, there have been several famous cases of inedia. Blessed Alexandrina de Costa of Balasar, Portugal, lived from 1904 to 1955. Although she was completely bedridden following a fall in 1918, she acted out the passion of Christ on Fridays from 1942 until her death in 1955. During the last thirteen years of her life, Blessed Alexandrina consumed no food or drink, only daily Eucharist. For three weeks in 1943, she was confined to a hospital in Oporto, Portugal, under scrutiny by doctors and nurses and round-the-clock supervision. It was ascertained that her fasting was complete except for the daily reception of the consecrated host. She was examined many times by several doctors and a psychiatrist.

Another example of inedia is the mystic Therese Neumann of Konnersreuth, Bavaria, Germany. Therese lived without food or water from 1922 until 1962, the year of her death. Thousands of U.S. Army liberation troops visited her in 1945 and 1946. She stated on one occasion that if she did not receive the Eucharist daily, she would surely die. She spoke Greek, Aramaic, Latin, and Hebrew during her ecstasies – languages she could not have acquired on her own.

The miracle of inedia proves that body and soul are one. A soul fed by divine life keeps a body alive without the need for any other nutrition. In some instances, such vitality can extend beyond this life and into the grave. Bodies who are extraordinary temples of the Holy Spirit sometimes remain intact after death. They do not compose in the natural way. Many such cases have been documented. I will borrow a few from Jean Carroll Cruz's book *The Incorruptibles*.

First, we should be clear that incorruptibility is not the same as the mummification practiced by the ancient Egyptians. In such cases, bodies are preserved with the use of chemical substances, wrappings, and salts. Nor is incorruptibility like the preservation that takes place in ice or bog regions. These days, as the ice caps melt, many bodies are being discovered in their original condition thanks to having been frozen. Incorruptibility is different. Bodies that *should* corrupt, *don't* corrupt. In some cases, these bodies, when living, had been subject to torture, dismemberment, and burning. They had been thrown into cisterns or rivers or buried in damp conditions alongside of decaying bodies. Their discovery was often accidental, usually during efforts to remove them to more convenient locations. In the case of deceased religious, often their habits had long disintegrated into sheds, while their bodies remained soft and pliable and their facial features intact.

Saints whose bodies have been found incorrupt were often famous in life for other manifestations of spiritual power: levitation, bilocation, the multiplication of food, drink, and money. In life and death, they could be surrounded by a pleasant smell called "the odor of sanctity." Today, many "incorruptibles" (the incorrupt bodies of saints) are available for public viewing. The small village of Nevers, France, is home to the incorrupt body of St. Bernadette Soubirous, the visionary of Lourdes (1844-1879). Her body has been preserved intact for over a hundred years without embalming or any other artificial means. After the first exhumation revealed its incorrupt state, a second exhumation in 1919, forty years after the saint's death, found the body in the same condition. The face, however, as a result of washing after the first exhumation, was slightly discolored. A wax worker was entrusted with the task of putting a thin covering of wax on the face. The body was placed in a coffin of glass and gold and can be viewed today in the Chapel of St. Bernadette in Nevers, France.

One of the most amazing preservations in history is surely that of St. Andrew Bobola (1598-1657). Prior to his martyrdom, St. Andrew was tortured extensively. Splinters of wood were driven under his nails before his hands were cut off, his face was mutilated almost beyond recognition, and he was flogged. The end came finally in the form of a sword blow to the neck. St. Andrew's body was hastily buried by the faithful in a vault below the Jesuit Church in Pinsk. When it was discovered forty years later, it was perfectly preserved despite open wounds which would normally foster corruption. Although his grave had been damp, causing his vestments to rot, and in spite of the proximity of decaying corpses, St. Andrew's body remained perfectly flexible, his flesh and muscle soft to the touch and the blood which covered his many wounds freshly congealed. The preservation was officially recognized by the Congregation of Rites in 1835. Even though this relic was roughly handled during its numerous transpositions, it was still in a remarkable state of preservation three hundred years later when the Bolsheviks attempted to destroy it. They disrobed the body and threw it on the floor. Eventually, it was sent by armed guard to Moscow where it was concealed by the Communist government in a museum. Pope Pius XI twice petitioned for the return of St. Andrew's body, and in 1923, a diplomatic courier to the Vatican Secretary of State was sent to search through medical museums where the militant atheists had set up derisive exhibitions of bishops. Upon discovery of the body in October 1923, the Pope successfully persuaded the government to release it. The body then traveled to Rome where it remained until the saint's canonization in 1938, after which it returned to Poland by way of Budapest, Cracow, and Warsaw.

The condition of St. Andrew Bobola's body, which has never been embalmed or treated in any way, was declared a miraculous preservation. Dr. Alexander Pascale (College Physicians of Rome) and Raymond Tarozzi (Professor of medicine in the University of Rome) stated in their medic-physical dissertations that the condition of the body would normally hasten dissolution since it was a corpulent specimen covered with wounds. The body was mutilated in many ways during the inhuman attack by the Cossacks. The ears, nose, lips, and parts of the fingers and one eye had been torn from the body. Large patches of skin had been ripped from the legs, leaving gaping wounds in which was found masses of congealed blood. The mutilated body was buried in summer, in a spot where the ground was moist, and nearby the contagious elements of decaying bodies. All of this would normally have acted on it to effect swift and thorough destruction. The doctors affirmed that no embalming of the body or other treatment had been administered. Yet, when they examined it, it had a normal color, was quite flexible, and had soft, lifelike skin.

Incorruptibility and inedia are two extreme examples of what is possible when the soul is fully alive in God. Just as the human body in perfect health can realize incredible feats of strength and speed, so can the soul filled with divine grace overcome evil, death, and decay. All that is required is a consistent effort – the daily "spiritual jogging" of prayer – and the application of our heavenly Trainer's guidelines, the Ten Commandments. Such a program will lead to spiritual vigor and triumph over the forces of evil within and without.

Epilogue

In December 2013, after 50 years in practice, I retired. Eileen and I took our first extended vacation in 61 years of marriage. Today, we have a home in Florida where we can escape Chicago winters and welcome on occasion our eight adult children, forty-six grandchildren, and five great-grandchildren.

My wife and I have stayed very active over the years in the causes important to us. We founded Illinois Right to Life and regularly volunteer with Birthright of Chicago, the Pro-Life Action League, Port Ministries, and the archdiocese's Respect Life Office. Of these, Port Ministries has a special place in our lives. My son Kevin has served as the president of the charity's board. It is very much a family affair.

I began this memoire with the observation that we are born into stories already in process, and that each of us will make a contribution to those stories in one way or another. The setting of my story has been, for the most part, Chicago and its environs. It was of great satisfaction to me to discover that my contributions in that area have been noted and appreciated. On May 17, 2014, I received the Presidential Award for Outstanding Merit at St. Mary's University of Minnesota. More exciting still, on May 22nd of that year, Eileen and I were joined by friends and family when the

Beverly/Morgan Park community honored me with an official street sign at 113th and Western Avenue: Dr. Dolehide Drive. I guess I have made my mark!

So many good memories…and so much to be grateful for! But my purpose here has been more than an attempt to leave my family a personal memoire. I have also wanted to testify to a larger audience of what I believe has been a significant and damaging shift in values over the last seventy years. I have approached this subject not as a philosopher or historian, but as a physician and family man. I saw firsthand, within my profession, the exchange of true human goods for fictions and lies. The Hippocratic Oath that stands for all that is best in medical care gradually took a backseat to a politics of profit and human exploitation.

I saw in the news this week that California has legalized assisted suicide. Just as with abortion, little by little the unthinkable becomes thinkable, and what was once a great evil becomes just another part of medical practice. We are on a slippery slope in this country when it comes to end of life issues. Part of this is a general disregard for the value of life, but partly responsible also is a broken economic system that cannot fund medical care. The quick answer, as with abortion, is to eliminate the person at the center of the equation.

I do not wish to end on a negative note, but a realistic appraisal of our society today does not leave much room for hope. I believe that the only answer for us is to turn back to God, to the Ten Commandments, and to the life of prayer. I know that the story of my life was written first and foremost by the hand of Divine Providence. I can bear witness that my faith brought me through hard times and good. It served as a light for my path and an ideal toward which I could strive. It's an old formula, but a simple one: faith, prayer, and good works. Around all these put love and you have a happy ending.

There are reasons for optimism. The nice thing about evil is that it eventually loses its sunny appearance and reveals itself for what it is. Abortion came on the scene as a remedy for women in crisis pregnancies. It was cloaked in the egalitarian language of "a woman's right to choose." Today, as statistics show, people are seeing the issue differently. Thanks to ultrasound and better education about gestational development and the brutal nature of abortion procedures, people today understand much better than the Roe v. Wade generation that a human life is truly present in the womb. This is a good paradigm of what can happen in all areas of human moral life. Science can be the instrument of increased awareness of fundamental goods that can never be violated without dire consequences for the individual and society. Those who are engaged in the medical sciences have special access to a knowledge that can lead our society back to sanity. The more we ask ourselves what constitutes human flourishing, the more we will arrive at a basic truth that – Lo and behold! – has always been available to us in the Hippocratic Oath and the teachings of the great religions: Life is an ultimate good to be cherished and protected. Heroic witness may be required in our time for this truth to take center stage again, but I firmly believe that heroic souls are working now to achieve this goal.

We are not short on heroism in our time, no more than in any other time in history. There are saints among us who daily take up the task of spreading the Gospel on earth and redeeming the temporal order through the blood of Christ.

Hence, I will end this story where I started, with a nod to my friend, Servant of God, Fr. John Hardon:

> Only heroic families will survive this war.
>
> Only heroic bishops, only heroic priests will survive this global conflict between the powers of darkness and the powers of light.
>
> Only heroic religious will be able to last.
>
> Only heroic men, women, and children will remain Catholics and Christians and faithful followers of the son of Mary